THE BIOLOGICAL TIME BOMB

THE BIOLOGICAL TIME BOMB

Gordon Rattray Taylor

AN  BOOK

The World Publishing Company
NEW YORK   CLEVELAND

PUBLISHED BY THE NEW AMERICAN LIBRARY, INC.
IN ASSOCIATION WITH
THE WORLD PUBLISHING CO.
2231 WEST 110TH STREET
CLEVELAND, OHIO

ORIGINALLY PUBLISHED IN GREAT BRITAIN
BY THAMES & HUDSON, LTD.

LIBRARY OF CONGRESS CATALOG CARD NUMBER: 68-31359

PRINTED IN THE UNITED STATES OF AMERICA

For Nicola and Michele,
with love and foreboding

Contents

Author's Note

The pace is quickening. Since I finished the manuscript of this book towards the end of 1967, important advances have taken place in several of the fields I examined.

The transplantation of organs, in particular, took a major step forward with the achievement of the world's first successful heart transplant operation. (I class an operation as successful if and when the patient is discharged from the hospital and able to resume, in some degree, a normal life.) Philip Blaiberg left the hospital in March 1968.

Sir Peter Medawar, director of Britain's National Institute of Medical Research, predicted that transplantation not only of hearts but of liver and lungs may be established practice within five years. Donald Douglas, Professor of Surgery at Dundee University, was another who gave five years as the period in which heart transplantation would become routine. He added that 70 percent of kidney transplants were doing well after two years at the last review.

Since heart disease is the commonest cause of death in advanced countries, this one step makes the question of how sufficient hearts are to be made available an urgent one. Dr. Marcelino Candau, Director General of the World Health Organisation, in March 1968 called for an international conference of doctors to define 'the ethical and practical questions involved' before governments introduced legislation on transplants of hearts or other organs. Meanwhile, in Britain, a move was made to change the law concerning transplants.

Such developments are predicted in *The Biological Time Bomb*. I hardly expected them to take place before the book was in print, however. Another prediction has not materialised so far: the clamant public demand for much wider provision of transplant facilities. It will not be long in coming.

Another area which has moved with unforeseen rapidity is the power to control the mind. It was announced during the year that anxiety had been found to be related to the presence in the blood of a chemical substance, sodium lactate.

This opens up the prospect of controlling neurotic anxiety: it also creates the possibility of inducing intolerable anxiety in instances of brainwashing—and just possibly a new military weapon. It would be convenient if one could make an enemy patrol nervous, or if one could get at the general in charge. In March Dr. K. E. Moyer of Pittsburgh University told a UNESCO conference on brain research that brain researchers 'stood on a threshhold similar to that on which the atomic physicist stood in the early 1940's'—thus practically taking the words out of my mouth He described brain operations which make it impossible for a person to be aggressive, and other techniques involving chemical or electrical intervention with the same effect. 'It is not inconceivable' he said, 'that specific antihostility agents can be placed in the water supply to make a peaceful population. This is, of course, frightening . . .' he added.

The prospects of raising intelligence were thought to have been weakened by a report by a South African doctor, Renée Liddicoat, throwing doubt on the efforts of Dr. Heyns' technique of abdominal decompression, described in Chapter 5, in raising intelligence. He suggested that the mothers in these experiments may have been above average in intelligence to begin with.

A more important reservation, to my mind, is whether the children will level off at the average level or above it when they reach adulthood. In other words, are they simply early developers? It is intelligence in the adult years that the world wants.

However, my belief that techniques for improving intelligence will be found does not depend merely on Dr. Heyns' work. Many other approaches are being tried, and currently interest is shifting back to better educational techniques such as the Responsive Environment method devised by Professor O. K. Moore of Pittsburgh, with its talking typewriter. Eventually, I am sure, the biological approach will make a breakthrough here. Yet one more area discussed in Chapter 5 has yielded advances: pain control. Thus a group of doctors at the National Heart Institute in Bethesda, Maryland, succeeded in mitigating the terrible pain of angina pectoris by electrical stimulation.

The production of 'carbon copy people' by cloning is a development of such enormous significance that it is worth noting that this process was extended from the group of plants such as dicots to the monocots (such as conifers) by the successful cloning of asparagus—thus lending weight to the belief it can be carried out with any type of cell.

It would be tedious and unnecessary to attempt to list all the advances in the past twelve months which bear on the work described in this book, but there are a couple more too important to omit. The news that an effective genetic code (nucleic acid) for a virus was created in the laboratory makes the manufacture of new man-made viruses an immediate possibility. In Britain's House of Lords, Lord Ritchie Calder, well known as an interpreter of science, warned the assembly of the danger of an all-lethal 'doomsday bug'—perhaps already in existence in the biological warfare establishments.

Even the remotest of the prospects discussed, that of creating higher forms of life in the laboratory, clicked one notch nearer when scientists found that the natural self-assembling tendency of the chemical units involved goes even further than they thought, each amino-acid having a preference for association with certain others. Furthermore, for the first time an enzyme, such as cells contain, was synthesised in the test-tube, without the aid of living cells. (Enzymes are the catalysts which regulate the processes of life.)

If this is what twelve months of biological research has notched up, what will the next twelve months bring? Certainly more, since each year the pace accelerates, as more people move into biology and as the total pattern of the life process becomes ever clearer.

The next ten years may reveal as much as the past fifty, and we shall have to absorb that knowledge. The problems are already piling up. Man must take decisive steps to cope with them without further delay.

G. R. T.

THE BIOLOGICAL TIME BOMB

1

Where Are Biologists Taking Us?

Two hundred years ago the French Encyclopaedist Diderot, in an iron-ical vision of the future which he called *The Dream of d'Alembert*, described how one day human embryos would be artificially cultivated and their hereditary endowment predetermined. His hero saw 'a warm room with the floor covered with little pots, and on each of these pots a label: soldiers, magistrates, philosophers, poets, potted courtesans, potted kings. . . .'

Today his vision no longer seems entirely fanciful, and some biologists believe that, before the end of the century at latest, it may be realized. Other writers – among them Shaw and Wells – have dreamed of the con-trol of growth, of tampering with memory and of the extension of the human life span to many centuries. None of these seems any longer to be so impossible of achievement. Indeed, some may be alarmingly close.

All these are biological advances. We are now, though we only dimly begin to realize the fact, in the opening stages of the Biological Revolution – a twentieth-century revolution which will affect human life far more profoundly than the great Mechanical Revolution of the nineteenth century or the Technological Revolution through which we are now passing.

For too long the public has maintained a false stereotype about biology: it was the science of classification, of botanizing and studying bees. Biologists were dry-as-dust creatures who studied the migrations of birds or dissected frogs to see how they tick. In contrast the physicist was seen as much more involved in reality. His tinkerings with sparks and wires produced, in due course, radio and television, not to mention the tele-phone. His interest in atoms seemed a little recondite at first but, sure enough, in due course, it produced the atom bomb and nuclear energy, and that is practical enough for anyone. But the biologist was different – biology was 'natural history', a subject for young ladies and elderly clergy-men.

This stereotype is about to be shattered. The biologists have got up their sleeves discoveries which have just as universal and earth-shaking an effect as those of the chemists and physicists. Attentive readers of the scientific journals have noticed, during the past five years or so, the appearance of a series of warning statements by eminent biologists – some made verbally at meetings or symposia, others in special articles or letters – warnings about the direction in which biology is heading.

The most active of the Cassandras has probably been the Californian biochemist Joshua Lederberg, Professor of Genetics at Stanford University, who has spoken in unusually definite terms on a number of occasions. Thus in 1966, in the *Bulletin of the Atomic Scientists*, he declared that 'a very consequential danger in life-span and the whole pattern of life are in the offing, providing that the momentum of existing scientific effort is maintained.'

Similarly Professor Bentley Glass, President of the American Society of Naturalists and one of the world's best-known investigators in the field of human genetics, has discussed what he calls 'the stupendous ethical problems which will face mankind in the very near future, as man begins to apply his knowledge to the control of his own reproduction and future evolution,' while the British Nobelist Francis Crick has pointed out that 'the development of biology is going to destroy to some extent our tradi-tional grounds for ethical beliefs, and it is not easy to see what to put in their place.'

Professor Salvador Luria is one of the father figures of American biology – an Italian who, since 1940, has worked in no fewer than five universities (Columbia, Vanderbilt, Princeton, Indiana and Illinois) before going on to Massachusetts Institute of Technology; he is one of the creators of modern virology. But he confesses to a feeling which 'has not been a feeling of optimism but one of tremendous fear' when he considers the potential dangers which would be created if man's new understanding of genetics were to be misapplied. In his contribution to *The Control of Human Heredity*, he urges that the scientist has a definite responsibility to 'prepare the public to cope with the foreseeable consequences of advances' in the subject.

But perhaps the strongest warning has come from the British ethologist Dr W. H. Thorpe of Cambridge University, one of the world's leading experts on animal behaviour, who declared recently: 'The ethical problems raised by the population explosion and artificial insemination, by genetics and neurophysiology, and by the social and mental sciences are at least as great as those arising from atomic energy and the H-bomb, from space travel and ultrasonic flight, from telecommunications, computers and automation. There is no doubt in my mind that several of these developments are as epoch-making for mankind as any that have preceded them. They rank at least as high, if not higher, in importance than the discovery of fire, of agriculture, the development of printing and the discovery of the wheel.'

More important than fire, printing and the wheel? One could hardly put it more strongly than that. What induces Dr Thorpe to make such a sweeping claim?

The discoveries he names have all radically changed man's way of life and the scope of his ability to influence his fellows. What the biologists have in store will certainly change our way of life too. Hitherto, for instance, it has been usual for a child to be born of two parents of differing sex, both of whom were alive at the time of his/her conception. Such tedious limitations are rapidly disappearing, with unforeseeable consequences for marriage and the family as we know it. Thanks to techniques for storing the male seed, it is already the case that a child may be conceived long after the death of the father. And a woman might bear a child to her great-grandfather one day. Indeed, research now in hand may make it possible for a woman to bear a child without male intervention, or even for a child to be born without the comfort of a maternal womb. The parents, if any, may be able to specify the sex of the child in advance, and even change it.

But these are simply advances in the single field of the reproductive process. In the field of ageing, gerontologists foresee both an extension of the life span and the preservation of a degree of youthful vigour into old age. Some even contemplate the possibility of immortality. Neurologists and others are exploring the brain, and hint at raising the level of intelligence, at improvement of memory and the control of moods and feelings. Geneticists are so confident of being able to tamper with heredity that they have begun to warn us to beware of them, while transplantation surgery has already begun to present us with ethical problems. Bio-chemists have even seriously proposed an attempt to synthesize life from inert materials. All these 'advances', it is evident, would have major social and ethical implications if they are really 'on'.

The difficulty which a writer faces in writing about such developments is that a general statement conveys only a feeble impression of the poten-tialities of the advance, whereas a concrete one appears hopelessly sensa-tional and even repellent. Thus if I say that grafting techniques may make body parts completely interchangeable I suggest little more than a medical advance. On the other hand, if I say that one day someone might say to you, indicating another person, 'I want you to meet my uncle and niece. They were in a car smash but fortunately the surgeon was able to get one complete body out of the undamaged bits', I am more likely to evoke incredulity than alarm.

I suspect that the immediate reaction of many people to such forecasts is that, if not downright impossible, they lie so far in the future as to be of no practical importance to people now living. Nothing could be farther from the truth, I regret to say. While some of the possibilities hinted at by biologists, such as the attainment of personal immortality, may lie a century or more in the future, it is certain that much of what they are doing will begin to bear fruit in the lifetime of those now living. For instance, the growing ability to control mental states is *already* facing us with problems such as the inability of young people to make a mature use of LSD. But this is not a once-for-all phenomenon. The hallucinogens are merely one of the first of an indefinitely long series of advances in the direction of mental control, and the present generation will certainly live to see many comparable problems as well as others less definable.

Again, the discovery of oral contraceptives is merely the *beginning* of a new world of expertise in the control of the reproductive process, and the controversies which have raged about the use of such pills will soon be lost in the thunder of even more desperate battles.

No one can say for sure when anything will be discovered, but it is fair to assume that at least *some* of the matters on which biologists all over the world are working will yield breakthroughs in the next five or ten years. For instance, there is an imminent prospect of being able to control the process by which the body rejects grafts of tissue from other organisms; this will make a wide range of transplantation operations possible. The heart transplantations which make news stories today should be viewed simply as the earliest advances in a long campaign. To look on such developments as complete and final is to repeat the complacency of the man who dismissed the automobile with the comment: 'Very clever, but it will never replace the horse.'

The fact is, we are all short on imagination. How many people, looking at a black bakelite telephone or brown bakelite switch-cover, thirty years ago, envisaged the world of brilliantly coloured plastics, both rigid and flexible, which we know today? Equally, it takes uncommon imagination to see in the hard-won and often unsatisfying biological achievements of today the fantastic possibilities which will be taken for granted by the generation of tomorrow. And I don't mean the day *after* tomorrow. Many of the possibilities discussed in this book, incredible as they may seem to some, will become realities only too soon.

It is therefore not merely interesting but socially important to try to evaluate them without delay.

But why do these barely credible developments threaten to burst upon us precisely now? What has been going on in the laboratories of the biologists that they have started to spew forth problems all much at the same time?

The biological breakthrough

Every science has a natural curve of development. At first it is burdened with erroneous pre-scientific beliefs and poses its problems wrongly: progress is slow. A slow gathering of carefully observed facts is the indispensable preliminary to the forming of generalizations. Then as insight is obtained, first in one sub-section, then in another, progress becomes more rapid. The various fields begin to coalesce and illuminate one another.

Physics and chemistry, being simpler and more uniform, entered on their growth sooner than biology. The word 'biology' was only coined at the beginning of the nineteenth century, when people began to see it as a discipline distinct from medicine, larger than 'natural history'. Before this time there had been no real awareness that a science of living things might constitute a coherent discipline. Work was predominantly observational and classificatory until the first great insights came in the first half of the nineteenth century: the cell theory of Schwann and Schleiden, which provided a common denominator for all forms of life, and the theory of evolution propounded by Chambers and Matthew (for which Darwin was soon to propose a suitable mechanism). Soon after came Mendel's work, neglected at the time, which opened up the study of heredity.

Progress also depends upon the availability of suitable tools. Until the achromatic microscope was devised early in the nineteenth century, the study of the cell was impossible, while the study of structures within the cell, such as the chromosomes, was dependent upon the apochromatic oil-immersion microscopes which did not become available until near the end of the century.

The fantastic quickening in the pace of biological research in the past few years is due, above all other factors, to the provision of new and extra-ordinarily powerful tools for the study of living things. Probably the chief among these is the electron microscope, which can magnify as much as a million times and reveal structures quite beyond the power of the light microscope to resolve. Seeing is believing, and a picture conveys in one instant information about shape, size, number, relative arrangement and other parameters, each of which might have to be deduced separately from tedious experiments, were no pictures available. It was not until after the last war that these instruments became commercially available.

Also important are various remarkably subtle and powerful methods of separating out the various components in a complex biological mixture. Not only the various parts of the cells of which all creatures are composed, but even various types and sizes of molecules can be sorted out, and often identified, by devices such as the ultracentrifuge, which exposes liquids to forces 100,000 times as great as gravity, or methods like electrophoresis, which sifts molecules with electric forces. Automation of many laboratory processes has also speeded work. In most biological laboratories today one will find machines which work all night as well as all day, tirelessly making measurement after measurement and recording them – or even calculating results from them. Because biology deals with such complex and delicate material, often present in vanishingly small quantities, it could not go far without techniques like these.

Still more, however, the breakthrough has been made possible by the growing sophistication of chemistry, which has proved able to explain the incredibly complex sequences of reactions within the cells of the body, as well as those which may take place in the blood, lymph and elsewhere, making biochemistry almost a separate discipline. We may, indeed, be moving into an era in which physics rather than chemistry will be needed to provide the necessary data to explain what happens at the cell surface, how muscles contract and how nerves conduct. Biophysics grinds even smaller than biochemistry.

Whatever the reason, it is fair to say that biology has moved into a phase of accelerated development to which it is not too much of an exaggeration to apply the word 'breakthrough'.

In so doing, it has also moved – as physics did earlier – into an era of million-dollar machines and large multi-disciplinary teams of specialists: cytologists, crystallographers, biochemists, neurologists, molecular biologists and a dozen more. The approach is no longer merely observational: instead the biologist makes hypotheses and devises experiments to test them. His measurements are made with the utmost precision and his approach is often statistical. The distinction between biology and medicine is rapidly becoming more acute.

However, blanket statements of this sort obscure the fact that biology is a group of disciplines, some of which are in a far more developed stage than others.

Biology, it can be said, seeks to answer seven distinct questions, and the pattern of this book is dictated by that fact, since each of these lines of development is advancing at a different rate. The questions can be briefly stated thus:

1 How did life of any kind originate?
2 What accounts for the variety of life forms (species)?
3 What is the nature of ageing and the cause of natural death?
4 How do living creatures function: what biochemical mechanisms do they depend upon? (Including: how do they resist infection?)
5 How is the behaviour of living creatures controlled? (Including: how does the brain work?)
6 How do living creatures replace themselves? (How does conception occur and what determines hereditary similarity?)
7 How do living creatures grow and develop? (Including: how does the egg develop within the womb?)

The nineteenth century saw one of these questions substantially answered – No. 2, What accounts for the variety of species? Recently we have seen the effective solution of another, No. 6. The details of fertilization and the mechanism of heredity are understood in considerable detail, even though there are some obscure points remaining to be cleared up. There has also been substantial progress on No. 4, the vast group of topics which we call physiology. Many of the social and ethical questions which are beginning to face us arise from progress in these two fields.

The problems which lie in the middle distance are those which derive from fields 3, 5 and 7: ageing and death, growth and development, hormones and the brain. Beyond them lies the ultimate question of the origin of life. But even here biologists begin to glimpse an answer.

I shall examine these fields in turn, starting with those which are already beginning to affect us and going on to the remoter or more speculative possibilities. Leaving aside the question of evolution, which caused such a furore in the last century, as a bomb which has already gone off, we are left with six sensitive areas – six bombs with smouldering fuses of varying lengths.

Biological control

The radical nature of what is happening can perhaps best be conveyed by a comparison. We can now create, on a commercial scale by chemical processes, substances which previously we had to look for in nature, and even substances which never previously existed. Whereas before we had to make do with what nature provided, now we can decide what we want; this may be called chemical control. Similarly, in the coming century, we shall achieve biological control: the power to say how much life, of what sort, shall exist where. We shall even be able to create forms of life which never existed before.

To some the prospect may seem terrifying, but as in all such advances, the new knowledge can be used for good or ill. The first consequences will certainly be a great extension of responsibilities. What was settled before, by chance or ineluctable circumstance, now becomes within our own power to regulate, and presents us with the need to take decisions – a task which many people find burdensome. Constant decision-making is the price of freedom. Part of the problem which faces us is to devise adequate institutions for taking the broader social decisions with which the mushrooming of biological knowledge most certainly is about to face us.

The mechanical revolution brought new freedoms to the ordinary man. Instead of having to spend his life in the area where he was born, it became easy for him to visit other parts of the country, to settle down in a chosen area, and still to maintain contacts with his family and childhood environment. True, this faced him with the necessity of actually *deciding* where to live, instead of accepting what the fates provided, but the responsibility was small compared with the benefits. Equally, of course, it led to a great deal of unnecessary travel, perhaps not worth the great technological investment which was needed to support it, and it certainly created new population movements and accelerated the drift to the towns, creating social problems there. The biological revolution will have comparable results.

Such knowledge will not only change our lives but will also, in so doing, change our industries. It will also affect the scale and direction of investment, and even the scale and direction of public taxation. We are now seeing the growth of a science-based industry which is primarily rooted in physics and, in particular, electronics. A second wave of science-based industry which is primarily biochemical, biophysical and biological will follow – where? Its forerunners are the small but immensely skilled firms which will now supply, often from stock, the most recondite biochemical substances, and the 'biomedical engineers' who devise ingenious machines for doctors, from radio pills to artificial kidneys. There will also be a vast expansion of medicine.

Agriculture will also be affected. The destruction of pests by releasing sterilized males, as was so successfully achieved by Dr Edward F. Knipling with the screw-worm fly, which formerly caused the loss of millions of dollars' worth of livestock every year, is but a pointer to the things to come.

To take a long look into the crystal ball may therefore be commercially smart as well as socially desirable.

There is also the military aspect. It was the British astronomer Fred Hoyle who said to me: 'I wouldn't go into biology if I were starting my life again now. In twenty years it is the biologists who will be working behind barbed wire.' The United States and Britain are known to have considerable establishments for the study of biological warfare. The American one is at Fort Detrick, the British at Porton Down. The American army also has plants, at Edgeworth Arsenal and elsewhere, for the manufacture of biological weapons, and several of these have been used in Vietnam. Such weapons can be deployed against crops and herds, as well as against men. How far other countries, and especially Russia and China, are pursuing similar activities remains shrouded in secrecy. It would be a pretty safe bet that they are, as may be some of the smaller bellicose countries. This might expand into a major branch of warfare.

Parallel with this runs the emergence of neurological war. Many countries are known to be manufacturing nerve-gases. U.S. generals have advocated the use of substances (among them, LSD-25) which may undermine the will to resist, claiming that a humane type of 'bloodless warfare' could be introduced. Important if true, but some people see another side to the question, and the issue needs clarifying.

All these advances, in fact, pose problems on which society ought to be making up its mind, and it is vital that it should do so before things have gone so far that they cannot be altered. The question of whether to regulate the world population size, and if so how and at what level, is merely one of the first of a great series of universal issues which need to be faced, and most of which are still being ignored.

In short, the biological revolution is certain to affect our lives, our safety and our happiness in a myriad ways.

Before it's too late

The biological revolution presents mankind with a group of quite new and extremely pressing questions. It is not often that a writer can use the word 'vital' without exaggeration, but these are truly vital matters – matters which affect our very lives.

Is this new accession of human know-how desirable? Will it actually conduce to greater human happiness? Even if it could, in principle, be so used, will man in fact have the sense to use it wisely or will he, as so often in the past, misuse it, creating biological slums and vital pollution to parallel the physical slums and chemical pollution which were the heavy price of the industrial revolution?

I call these new questions because, until the advent of the atomic bomb, the conviction that all knowledge was to the good and that scientific research promised overwhelming benefits for man was generally held. The idea of forbidding a line of research did not receive serious discussion, nor did anyone hesitate to publish his results for any but reasons of commercial advantage. But today the release of nuclear forces is seen by many people as entailing risks which outweigh any conceivable advantage. And it has actually happened that scientists have avoided publicizing procedures which would bring the power to make nuclear weapons within the reach of small groups.

Some psychologists feel compunction about publicizing all they know about control of the mind, for fear that such knowledge will be abused and used for 'brainwashing' or similar purposes. Quite a number of the developments I am about to describe could be equally misused, either through malice or stupidity, or both. So the question of whether such work should proceed unsupervised and uncontrolled is real and urgent. There is still time to stop. Soon it will be too late, even if we wish to. These issues must therefore be considered now.

The feeling that some kinds of knowledge are too dangerous for man, at least in his current state of social and intellectual development, is founded, I think, on the belief that he is more likely to use new power for ill than for good. Or perhaps we should say that more people will misuse the new powers, or that they will be misused more often, than they will be used for good. Or, simply, that misuse could have consequences so serious as to outweigh any possible advantages of wise use. This is what we feel about nuclear warfare. The costs and misery caused by a nuclear war would so far outweigh the advantages of cheaper power for civil purposes, that only a vanishingly small risk of misuse is acceptable.

Are the new biological powers of this character? How serious are the consequences of misuse? How likely is misuse to occur? Since only a confirmed optimist would bet on men – some men, somewhere – not misusing powers, the question of whether we could impose some kind of control on biological research is not an academic one.

Apart from the actual misuse of new powers, whether by accident or design, there is a contingent question of extreme importance. How great a rate of change can society stand? It takes time to adjust to new social conditions, and when the rate of innovation is rapid, the disruption caused can destroy a culture, as has often been seen when western culture has impinged on technologically primitive societies. (There are curious parallels between the response of western youth to hallucinogenic drugs like LSD and the response of South Sea Islanders to alcohol.) It seems quite possible that the rate of biological innovation may be so high as to destroy western civilization, perhaps even world culture, from within, creating a disorientated, unhappy and unproductive society, unless it is brought under deliberate control.

Control could take two forms. Either the scope and direction of research could be controlled, or research could be left free, but its findings could be placed in the ice-box and brought out for practical application only when and as desired. In practice a combination of both would be needed, since even a rigorous control of research could not prevent the occurrence of unscheduled discoveries. But, of course, both types of control would be immensely difficult to apply, and could very easily be the source of abuse and misjudgment. So much so, that many people would prefer to take a chance on the dangers of uncontrolled research rather than face the limitations of control. Certainly, almost all scientists would take this view.

This being so, we are obliged to face up to the converse set of implications. If the rate of change is to be high, and especially if it is unlimited, could we improve our capacity to adapt? Under present conditions, when an innovation is made, it is launched into use without any preliminary social readjustment. A good example is artificial insemination. This, as we shall see in the next chapter, creates problems of a legal kind: for instance, does the child of an artificially inseminated mother inherit property from its legal father? But instead of clarifying the law on this and similar points *before* making the technique available, we have introduced the technique and left the law – to say nothing of the social and personal implications – to sort themselves out as best they can, a process which is now occurring at a considerable cost in time, money, heartbreak and injustice as between different cases.

Having surveyed the work of biologists in many countries, having listened to their own comments on the implications of such work, to me at least it is clear that the social and personal costs of adapting to this new knowledge will be terrifyingly, unacceptably high unless we make a major, conscious effort to regulate the pace and scope of development, instead of letting it control us.

Apparently it is not in human nature to consider making major social adjustments before the shoe actually pinches: indeed, it often has to go on pinching a long time before inertia and vested interest are overcome. A more telling instance than artificial insemination is the need for many more kidney dialysis machines, for lack of which large numbers of people are now dying. Only the first stirrings of a public demand that something be done about this situation are so far felt. One cannot avoid the conclusion that the public will not begin to make provision for the many other strange developments described in this book until the problems are dumped, howling, on their doorstep.

I am therefore forced to the conclusion that society will have to control the pace of research, if it can, and will certainly have to regulate the release of these new powers. There will have to be a biological 'ice-box' in which the new techniques can be placed until society is ready for them. This is not a conclusion to my taste at all. I do not feel in the least optimistic about our prospects of exerting such control without serious muddles and abuses. Nevertheless, the social consequences of what is in the pipeline could be so disastrous – nothing less than the break-up of civilization as we know it – that the attempt must be made.

In the following chapters I shall try to justify this assertion, as a basis for discussing in more detail what we might, and should, do about it. The writing is on the wall: it is urgently necessary that someone should make an attempt to interpret it.

2

Is Sex Necessary?

Biology has already begun to transform one area of life of the greatest importance; the process by which living things reproduce themselves. In recent years, new methods of contraception, artificial insemination coupled with the prolonged storage of spermatozoa, and, most recently, restoration of fertility in certain types of infertility have been the subject of widespread comment, and some controversy. How much further this process has to go is what I shall now do my best to explain.

The case of contraception is important as a paradigm of what other biological advances may bring. The dual implications – at the personal and the political levels both – look like being a portent of what we shall experience elsewhere.

Contraceptive devices have begun to change the patterns of social behaviour in the west, making pre-marital sexual experience commoner as well as altering the size of families (notably in Catholic areas) and the spacing of children as well as the stage in the mother's life at which they appear. In addition to the effect on the individual, contraception has created political and demographic problems. By making it *possible* to control the population explosion, it has created a responsibility to decide on levels, to obtain agreement on an international scale and to find means of inducing people – who may be miserably poor or uneducated, or bound by age-old customs – to adopt the methods which biology has evolved.

But the fact is, biological science is taking the reproductive process apart in a far more thorough way than is yet generally understood. Merely to block the mechanism of reproduction is the crudest kind of intervention –

little more than stopping a machine by putting a spanner in the works. The oral contraceptive represents the pay-off of work on steroid hormones which started with discoveries before World War I. In the twenties and thirties many of these hormones were isolated and their chemical structure worked out; methods of making them artificially were devised. This led to the devising of variants on what nature provides: new hor- mones such as the world had never possessed before. After World War II the clinical effects of these new molecular structures were explored, a phase of development which still continues.

This gives us a time-scale. Fifty or sixty years from the initial discovery to major social impact; twenty-five or thirty years from intensive laboratory studies. Much of what this chapter is about concerns work which is still in the second, or even the first of these phases. If large sums of money are made available, no doubt the time to application will be shortened; and probably it will be shortened in any case because biological science as a whole is now more generously supported than it was thirty years ago and discoveries in one field often throw light on what is happening in another.

The kind of applications which might result from a thorough under- standing of the reproductive process in all its aspects are likely to be vastly more far-reaching than these early spanner-in-the-works attempts at intervention. One of the most extraordinary of the possibilities now being explored has already received some press attention: it has been reported under such headlines as 'Einsteins from Cuttings' and 'J'aime Mozart XXIII'. More scientifically, it is referred to as 'cloning people'. When, some five years ago, a scientist at Cornell reported his first results, they received only a flicker of publicity, but they might prove the starting-point of something which could affect the whole status of plant, animal and human life on earth. As one leading biologist, Joshua Lederberg, has commented we may be 'on the brink of a major evolutionary pertur- bation'.

The scientist was Professor F. C. Steward, Director of the Laboratory for Cell Physiology, Growth and Development at Cornell University, a chemist who was once Director of Aircraft Equipment for the British Ministry of Aircraft Production in World War II. What he did was to take cells from a carrot root – the part you eat – and place them in a slowly rotating tube, which bathed them in a nutrient medium of which the most unusual constituent was coconut milk. 'We were hardly prepared', he has written, 'for the dramatic effects on the quiescent carrot cells.' The tissue began to grow rapidly. In less than three weeks it had multiplied in weight some eighty-fold. 'It was', he says, 'as if the coconut milk had acted like a clutch, putting the cell's idling engine of growth into gear. . . .'

After various experiments with other growth-stimulating substances, the research entered a second phase. Up to a hundred of these carrot 'explants' were being cultured in a single vessel. Some of the cells would break away from the main mass. These followed varying courses. Some grew to giant size. Some formed filaments, by successive division. Some formed buds, like yeast cells. And some – and this is the nub of the story – formed clumps which began to put out roots. Transferred to a solid medium, they began to put up green shoots. Transferred again to soil, and nursed along, they matured into carrot plants, with normal roots, stalks, flowers and seeds.

Seventy years ago, the Austrian biologist G. Haberlandt had dreamed that such 'vegetative reproduction' might one day be possible. Steward has now realized his vision. Later experiments showed that almost any of the cells from an early carrot embryo can be made to grow vegetatively in this way. Steward estimated that he had got more than 100,000 embryoids on one plate of agar jelly which had been inoculated with a solution of cells from a single carrot embryo.

Since Steward's breakthrough, other workers have succeeded in performing a similar experiment with tobacco plants. A slightly different routine of culture had to be worked out: it seems that the requirements of each plant may be quite precise. The current presumption is that, before long, it will be possible to perform a similar trick with any such plant material – or, at the least, with a majority. The sixty-four-thousand-dollar question, of course, is whether the same trick can be done with animal cells. Biologists see no reason why not, although to carry the embryo thus generated to maturity in the lab. would require techniques which are not yet available.

The culturing of cells in the laboratory is, in itself, by no means a new technique. It is only a dozen years, however, since means were found of growing a sheet of tissue starting with only a single cell. Normally, a single cell, placed in nutrient medium, fails to divide. The late Wilton

Earle, arguing that a cell might need the presence of others because they diffused some chemical substance into the medium, concluded that the substance oozing from a single cell would diffuse away and become diluted until it could not affect the cell from which it came. He therefore confined single cells in narrow tubes. Almost at once they began to divide.

But these cultured cells show little desire to form themselves into organs or other bodily structures. Organ formation seems to depend on influences, probably chemical in nature, from adjacent tissues of another kind. The kidney cells will arrange themselves into tubules provided that spinal cord tissue is present. The nature of these influences is under study. Once organs are formed, however, they can be maintained in culture and will increase in size. But the bridge between cell culture and organ culture has still to be built.

It would be over-optimistic therefore, I suspect, to assume that the vegetative culture of animal cells up to the point of an entire organism will prove anything like as easy as in the case of carrots.

Nevertheless, this work has been of immense value to biologists. Simply to have tissues available in the laboratory, the characteristics of which are known, makes it possible to test the effect of various growth-promoters, inhibitors, hormones and other agents, without confusing the experiment by influences from the rest of the organism, as happens when such experiments are performed on animals or men. What is particularly valuable is to have a mass of cells derived from a single cell, since all these cells are genetically identical, and the work is not confused by genetic variations. Such a genetically uniform mass of cells is known as a clone, from a Greek word meaning 'throng'. Steward's work has therefore been described as 'cloning' carrots. The operation to which Lederberg has looked forward with some apprehension has been called 'cloning people'.

There is another method of vegetative reproduction well known to horticulturalists – the taking of cuttings. (Here again the offspring are genetically identical with the parent plant.) By journalistic licence, the cloning of people has been called 'people from cuttings', a somewhat misleading description. If the vegetative reproduction of people is ever achieved, it is much more likely that it will be done by taking a few cells from an early embryo than by shaving off a piece of skin, say, and growing on from there. The more specialized a cell has become, the harder it is likely to be to force it back up the stream of development to the unspecialized state from which could be derived, by re-specializations, the whole range of specialized cells – nerve cells, kidney cells, muscle cells, and so on – which go to make up a living body.

The essential point, however, is the genetic unity of any such clone. For animal breeders, obviously, such a method would have enormous attractions: it would enable them to produce absolute duplicates of any specially successful bull, sheep or what-have-you, on whatever scale was required and without delay. Obviously it will be made use of the moment it is practical. But it has a disadvantage: if animals are produced in this way on a large scale, the normal processes of evolution are balked. Plant and animal breeders know already that a combination of sexual and vegetative reproduction is necessary to produce the most satisfactory strains. It is claimed that crossing two strains results in 'hybrid vigour', although the scientific basis of this is somewhat obscure. The argument applies far more strongly if people are produced in this way, for the misfits cannot be junked. Thus the evolutionary process is set aside, with consequences it is hard to foresee in any detail. Hence Lederberg's remark, quoted earlier.

However, before evolutionary problems manifest, we are likely to face quite pressing social and personal problems, and how far we go towards the eventual problems will depend on how far we can integrate such methods into our culture; some countries may even decide to reject them and to prohibit such a mode of reproduction. But, as with many other biological developments which will be discussed in this book, the decision may not lie with the west. If an oriental despot should decide that he could produce more rugged soldiers, more brilliant scientists, more skilful workmen or more fertile women by such techniques, he might pour the necessary resources into making them practicable, and then impose them. The problem which would face the western civilizations would then be whether to compete or perhaps face extinction – culturally if not militarily.

This technique, as the reader will have realized, raises in an acute form all the problems traditionally associated with eugenics. Unanswered questions spring up like foes from dragon's teeth. From whom should one take the cell from which a hundred thousand duplicate progeny will be bred? (With what intensive scrutiny society will look at the first products of such an experiment!) How will the members of this new caste themselves feel about it? Will they be an élite group, only permitted to marry among one another in a sort of mass incest? If not, if they marry freely with uncloned people, the virtues of their carefully selected heredity will be dissipated – though of course there will be some upgrading of the general level by dispersing the desired genes. Or will they be forbidden to marry outside the clone, perhaps?

Members of a clonal group will enjoy an important advantage: like identical twins, they will be able to accept grafts of tissue or whole organs from one another. Apart from the much greater security of life this will give them in general, such an advantage might be supremely important among a small isolated group, such as astronauts on a mission lasting several years, and, at least until such time as the problems of graft rejection are overcome (a subject discussed in Chapter 3), it will be an obvious matter of policy to select teams in this way. Indeed there may be another good reason for doing so.

At present the only genetically identical groups with which we are acquainted are twins, triplets and the rare higher orders of identical twindom. There is some evidence that identical (or one-egg) twins have a peculiar sympathetic awareness of each other's needs and problems – even, it has been claimed, a psychic awareness amounting to thought transference. It is certainly true that twins brought up in widely different circumstances have often lived closely similar lives, marrying similar partners of similar ages, and this is so even when they have not been in communication with one another. It is not mere sensationalism, therefore, to ask whether the members of human clones may feel particularly united, and be able to co-operate better, even if they are not in actual supersensory communication with one another.

Ability to work as a team is important in some sports, like mountainclimbing, in some military activities – one can think of a raiding party or a bomber crew – and probably in groups of people working under water on the lines pioneered by Cousteau in France or the SEALAB experiment off the California coast, since communication is particularly difficult in such conditions. A group of astronauts spread out over the surface of a remote planet provides another example. It follows that there are many parties, from the Space Agency to the manager of an ice-hockey team, which may have a direct interest in supporting research into this kind of biological development.

The late Professor J. B. S. Haldane, one of the most brilliant and practical scientists of our time, was one of those who took the possibility of cloning people quite seriously. In his view 'we may find out at any moment' how to induce cultured cells to organize themselves, as we already have done with the plants, and this could 'raise the possibilities of human achievement dramatically'. Haldane declared that most clones will be made from people of at least 50, except for athletes and dancers, who would be cloned younger. They will be made from people who have excelled in some socially acceptable accomplishment, though we shall have to be careful that their success wasn't due to mere accident. Equally useful, he said, might be the cloning of people with rare capacities, even if their value was problematic – for instance, people with permanent dark adaptation, people who lack the pain sense, those who can detect what is happening in their viscera and even control it, as some eastern yogis can.

Haldane also produced the interesting suggestion that centenarians should be cloned, provided they were 'reasonably healthy'. Not that longevity is necessarily desirable in itself, but data on its desirability are needed. He was struck by the fact that many exceptional people have unhappy childhoods and some are permanently deformed by this experi- ence. He held that after the age of 55 great geniuses would spend their time in educating their clonal offspring, which he thought would avoid some of the frustration the latter might have felt. Others may think that geniuses do not necessarily make good parents, even that some degree of frustration is required to provide the motive force which drives genius. One more point should be made. As the French biologist Jean Rostand has pointed out, to print off a human being in hundreds or thousands of copies is in a sense to confer immortality upon him, for these offspring can of course be cloned in their turn, indefinitely.

Lord Rothschild, for long a Cambridge physiologist and an inter- national authority on the structure and action of spermatozoa, left his bench and became a businessman, working for one of the largest chemical concerns in the world. In this dual role, he is, one may assume, unlikely to speak wildly or sensationally. Yet in 1967 he told scientists at the Weiz- mann Institute of Science in Israel that he regarded cloning people as a near possibility. The problem he foresees is whether everyone should be

allowed to clone themselves if they wish, and he expects to see a Commis/
sion for Genetical Control established to vet applications. One can
imagine the devious manoeuvres to which the more ego/centred members
of the population might go in order to reduplicate themselves indefinitely.
Twenty/three Mozarts would scarcely be tolerable: twenty/three Hitlers
or Stalins at once hardly bear thinking about.

Steward's approach has a classic simplicity which allows the dramatic
nature of his results to emerge clearly. But biology does not always pro/
ceed by simple means, and it is very possible that cloning of animals will
only be achieved by more complicated methods. A glimpse of the
possibilities is given by the work of Dr J. B. Gurdon of Oxford Univer/
sity. Gurdon has managed, by a technique which spillikins players
might envy, to take the nucleus out of an intestinal cell of a frog – the
nucleus is the control/centre containing the chromosomes – and to
implant it in an unfertilized frog egg, the nucleus of which has been
destroyed by a tiny beam of radiation. Would the egg with its cuckoo
nucleus develop? He found that such eggs develop just as though they
had been fertilized normally and in some cases reach the tadpole stage
successfully.

The important point established by this experiment is that the special/
ized intestinal cell nevertheless still contains all the genetic information
needed to build a tadpole. Although much of this information has been
'switched off', as being unneeded by an intestinal cell, it has, as the
experiment demonstrates, not been destroyed. Thus the potentiality of
producing adults from body/cells (as distinct from germ/cells, i.e. eggs
and spermatozoa) is there. Furthermore, the resulting creatures have only
one parent, genetically speaking: the frog, be it male or female, from which
the intestinal cell was taken; and the offspring are identical with the
parent just as if they were identical twins. The tadpoles thus produced
become frogs and, despite their unusual hereditary complement, repro/
duce in the normal way.

Gurdon's technique accordingly holds out the possibility, *right away*,
of producing exact copies of prize bulls, race/winning horses, or excep/
tional human beings. So far no one has succeeded in doing this, partly
because mammalian eggs are almost invisibly small (about one hundredth
of an inch in diameter, in the case of man) which makes the cellular
surgery involved exceptionally difficult. But already techniques for

removing structures almost as small are in existence. And, as one commentator observed, compared with the ethical problems raised, the scientific ones are trivial.

Genetically uniform populations could also be produced, in principle, by another technique closely akin to the one we have been discussing, but narrower in range: parthenogenetic conception or virgin birth.

Parthenogenesis was achieved in sea-urchins as long ago as 1899, by the French, later American, biologist Jacques Loeb. 'When I announced the successful chemical fertilization of sea-urchins,' Loeb recalled, 'the almost unanimous opinion was that I had been the victim of an illusion, and at first I myself was afraid that I had been mistaken.' Scientific periodicals of the day, like the *Annales des Sciences Naturelles*, were ironical at the expense of what they dubbed 'chemical citizens, the sons of Madame Sea-Urchin and Monsieur Chloride of Magnesium'. But before long another French scientist, Eugène Bataillon, had repeated the feat with a much higher order of creature, the frog. He too was almost unable to believe his eyes, and as he watched the first fatherless tadpoles fluttering about in his test-tubes, was gnawed by the fear that frog-sperm might somehow have been present in the tap-water he had used.

Such experiments showed that even a simple mechanical stimulus, such as the prick of a needle, may be enough to start the egg dividing, but that usually development does not proceed very far. When eggs are formed they receive from their parent cells only a half complement of the chromosomes – the structures which carry the genetic message. The same occurs when sperm are formed, so that, when egg and sperm fuse, the number of chromosomes is restored to normal, and the offspring has received genetic instructions from both parents. It therefore shows a mixture of parental characteristics, some from the father, some from the mother, and others a combination of the two. The egg which starts developing parthenogenetically, on the other hand, has only half the normal number of chromosomes, and it may be that, in complex organisms, this is sufficient to abort development. The cloned cell, in contrast – being derived from a body-cell, not a germ-cell – has no such handicap. Moreover, the problem of how to nurture the cloned cell, or the artificially launched egg, may soon be resolved by another recently developed technique.

Artificial inovulation

In 1962, the world saw something never seen before, something recalling the kind of wild rumours which used to circulate in the Dark Ages. Two South African Dorper ewes gave birth to two healthy Border Leicester lambs. Moreover, the fathers of these lambs had never left England. The achievement was reported in the *Journal of Reproduction and Fertility* under the flat title 'Successful Long-Distance Aerial Transportation of Fertilized Sheep Ova'.

The eggs had been flown to South Africa nestling in the oviduct of a living rabbit, which had maintained them in the requisite physiological conditions.

It is barely a dozen years since L. E. Rowson at the Agricultural Research Council's station near Cambridge began, with others, to study the transfer of eggs from one animal to another. It promised to provide a valuable way of improving breeds of livestock, since it would enable a high-grade female animal to produce more of her own offspring than is normally possible. All animals are capable of producing far more eggs than they will ever need. Nature provides a vast surplus of immature eggs, just as it does in human beings. By injecting FSH, the hormone which normally releases eggs from the ovary, cows can be induced to release forty or more eggs in a single cycle. (This is termed 'superovulation'.) If these can be placed in the womb of other animals, to be brought to term, the prize-winning sheep can be made to produce offspring at the rate of several hundreds a year. The process thus represents the converse of artificial insemination, which now enables a prize bull to father more than 50,000 offspring in a year. It is referred to as 'artificial inovulation'.

Since Rowson's original experiment, eggs have been flown to the United States and other countries, and they have also been transferred between different strains of animal. Under Rowson's guidance, a white rabbit gave birth to black offspring, and later a Friesian cow gave birth to a Hereford calf.

The process still presents some difficulties: in the cow, for instance, it is difficult to induce the follicles holding the extra eggs to rupture, and it may be that the ratio of two or more of the hormones involved is of critical importance. Also, if the number of eggs shed becomes too large, the percentage which becomes fertilized declines.

At first, it was necessary to perform a minor surgical operation, resembling Caesarean section, to recover the eggs, and another to reimplant them. But in 1964 Japanese workers at the Livestock Industry Experimental Station operated by the Japanese Ministry of Agriculture succeeded in making a transfer without surgical methods, and produced a healthy calf. The eggs were washed out of the donor cow and one was injected into a cow's uterus with a special double syringe, one barrel of which introduces carbon dioxide gas into the uterus, thus distending it, while the other injects the egg at the right moment.

Artificial inovulation offers other prospects besides stock improvement. It may make it possible to discover why prenatal mortality is high in some domestic animals and, apart from facilitating genetic studies, it holds out hope of alleviating certain types of human sterility.

An essential feature of the method is that the receiving uterus shall be, within a day either way, at the same stage of the monthly cycle as the donor uterus at the time at which the egg is removed. (Why this matters is still obscure.) Problems like these can be studied by placing plastic eggs which have been made radioactive in the uterus or oviduct. Their course can then be followed by tracing the radioactivity.

While there are many types of infertility, including complete inability to produce eggs, a certain proportion of infertile women have a suitable supply of eggs, but their oviducts are blocked and the eggs cannot get to the uterus. Inovulation would get round this, provided some of the oviduct was open – for it is in the oviduct that fertilization takes place.

Professor A. J. Parkes, Marshall Professor of the Physiology of Reproduction at Cambridge University, has discussed the point in his work *Sex, Science and Society*. After referring to the difficulties already discussed, he commented: 'However, all these problems will be solved one day or other, and the transference of eggs of the required sex will be possible in man in the course of time.' As things stand today, there is nothing to stop a surgeon with the requisite knowledge attempting such a transfer on a willing patient except lack of courage. The risk to health involved is minimal, and there is little reason to suppose that the resulting child would not be fully healthy and normal, least of all where a woman is implanted with one of her own eggs.

It seems, therefore, that we must reckon very shortly with the avail-ability of a female form of AI, and equally of AID, where the letters stand for Artificial Inovulation, Donor instead of Artificial Insemination, Donor. Perhaps we shall have to write AID ♀ and AID ♂. The discussions which raged round the latter when it was first used in man will no doubt rage round the newer technique, though perhaps less fiercely, since unconscious fears about female unchastity are not so deeply involved.

A tense situation could arise, however, if, as with the Friesian cow which bore a Hereford calf, a white woman gave birth to a coloured child, or vice versa.

Storage of eggs and sperm

The flexibility of the new techniques of inovulation, insemination and test-tube fertilization obviously depends rather closely on how far eggs and sperm can be kept in storage without damage.

Many people imagine that it is simply a question of placing a test-tube of the material in the deep freeze, but actually the process is far from simple. Early experiments in storing semen proved failures and no pro-gress was made until workers at the National Institute of Medical Research in England found that damage could be averted if the sperm were placed in glycerol first. Even so, freezing had to be at a predetermined rate. And while the seed of bulls proved tough enough to stand up to storage in this way, that of several other domestic animals proved more fragile.

When many millions of dairy cattle had been successfully bred using frozen semen without any increase in the proportion of abnormal off-spring, physiologists began to consider seriously the possibility of similar storage of human seed. The immediate application of such a technique might be to pool the semen of infertile men, who produce only a small proportion of active spermatozoa, until the fluid was concentrated enough to cause fertilization. More remotely, eugenists saw in sperm-storage a technique of eugenesis: the seed of exceptional people might be stored and doled out to a large number of women, in an attempt to improve the quality of the race. (The pros and cons of such a project are discussed in a later chapter.)

For several years, however, no very serious attempt to explore the possibilities of storing human semen were made. As Professor Parkes has observed: 'Work on the preservation of human spermatozoa has not been pursued with the vigour which the interests of the subject seem to justify. . . . mainly it seems to arise from a lack of enthusiasm for the idea of abolishing in human reproduction the need for contemporaneous and contiguous action on the part of the two sexes.' In plainer words, people like snogging.

It seems that the first medical scientists to risk the clinical use of stored sperm were Drs Iizuka and Sawada, who reported that over two dozen children had been successfully produced in this way in 1958. Later, a similar course was taken by a Philadelphia doctor, using sperm stored for periods of up to two years to fertilize a small number of women whose husbands were infertile. Little was published about the results, but I understand that none of the children, now about three years old, shows any defect or weakness attributable to the process. Recently, the director of Michigan University's Center for Research in Reproductive Biology was more forthcoming. In 1967 he reported to the state society of Obstetricians and Gynecologists that 18 of 44 women who had received sperm frozen for more than 18 months had become pregnant. None of these children, as regular examination shows, has exhibited any defects traceable to the sperm. Dr S. J. Behrman summed up this achievement triumphantly: 'What we have done so far is to freeze the male cell . . . to suspend this life for up to two and one-half years and still obtain successful pregnancies. There is every reason at the moment to believe that this suspension can be prolonged indefinitely.' He could have added that bull semen has now been stored for periods over ten years without either undergoing genetic damage, or showing more than slight loss of vitality.

There is one factor no one cares to mention which makes it very likely that such experiments will be continued and extended: the probability that, in the event of nuclear war, the germ cells of many men – perhaps even a majority of the male population – will suffer radiation damage, and so come to transmit genetic defects which could persist for many generations. In such emergency circumstances, the government might urge, or even try to compel, women to avoid conception, except by insemination with undamaged sperm which had been stored under lead shielding at the bottom of mine-shafts or in other places where radiation could not penetrate. Governments must already be considering such precautions, and a nation-wide appeal to donate sperm, as well as blood, may be issued, if time permits, at the start of any such future war.

It would, of course, be equally desirable to store undamaged eggs, as well as sperm, but at present no effective techniques of egg storage for any prolonged period appear to exist. The eggs which L. E. Rowson sent to South Africa and America would survive up to eight days in the oviduct of rabbits. By lowering the temperature to 8–10° C, sheep eggs have been successfully stored for up to 72 hours. But freezing the egg destroys it, so we seem to be somewhat remote from this particular possibility at present.

There is, however, an alternative possibility: whole ovaries may be maintained in tissue culture In 1966 Dr Theodore Fainstat of the Strangeways Laboratory near Cambridge reported that, by reducing the oxygen supply, mammalian ovaries had been maintained for several weeks: the exact oxygen level required seems to depend on the stage of development the ovary is in when it is removed from the body. Meanwhile other workers are attempting to culture single cells from the ovary, and in particular those cells which eventually give rise to eggs. So far they have been induced only to yield the hormone progesterone. The prospect, therefore, that an ovum bank will eventually become feasible must be taken seriously.

Test-tube babies

Since both eggs and spermatozoa are freely available, it might seem a simple step to bring them together in a test-tube and effect fertilization, thus producing the 'test-tube baby' which so obsesses the popular press. (The term was widely used when human artificial insemination first became an issue, though no test-tubes are involved at any point in the process, and it is difficult to see what terminology journalists will have left unused when a genuine test-tube baby arrives.)

But in fact this feat is difficult, and no one has been able to perform it reliably, though a Cambridge physiologist, Dr R. G. Edwards, has had occasional successes (using pigs as his experimental animals) and may be on the brink of a breakthrough. Edwards declares: 'We may shortly be able to obtain numbers of human embryos in the process of cleaving.' There are, he explains, two main difficulties. First, the eggs have to pass through certain stages of development before they are ready for fertilization. All the eggs which the ovary will release, and more, have been formed by birth – up to half a million of them. But they are not yet in fully developed form; these potential eggs are known as oocytes, or egg-cells. They require to divide at least twice more, and the first of these divisions is a peculiar one, known as meiosis, in which the genetic material in the egg is halved in quantity. (Genetic material is also halved when the sperm is formed, so that when the two fuse, the quantity is restored to normal.) Two further divisions take place, and three of the resulting cells are abandoned, only one going on to form the egg. The reason for this is unknown.

This second stage only occurs after puberty, when hormones known as gonadotrophins are secreted into the bloodstream, on a monthly rhythm, which bring it about, and cause one egg to be released into the oviduct. (Why all the oocytes are not stimulated simultaneously is also unknown.)

Edwards was able to get his pig oocytes through this second stage, and also achieved this with human ova.

But there is a second difficulty. Spermatozoa also undergo some obscure change before they become effective; it has been dubbed 'capacita-tion' since it gives them the capacity to fertilize, but its nature is a mystery. It is believed that some secretion of the female effects capacitation. Edwards tried taking human sperm 10 hours after coitus, hoping that it would by then have been capacitated, but without success. He also tried putting the human egg and sperm into the oviduct of a rabbit, think-ing that this might provide a cosier environment than a test-tube. Also no go, although there were a few cases where the sperm penetrated the egg.

However, an American team believes that it has found the stuff which capacitates rabbit sperm (an enzyme called beta-amylase). If so, test-tube fertilization is just around the corner, or nearer. Maintained in a test-tube, development does not proceed far, but another recourse is open: to implant the fertilized egg in the uterus by the techniques already described.

The most immediate application of such a technique would be to help married couples handicapped by certain types of infertility. While in-fertility may have a variety of causes, including complete failure to pro-duce eggs on the part of the woman or complete failure to produce sperm on the part of the man, these extreme instances are rare. More commonly, the man produces only a small number of efficient sperm, mixed with malformed or ineffective ones. In such a case, exposure of the ovum derived from the wife to the male sperm could be continued until fertilization was seen to have taken place, when the egg would be reimplanted. Again, there would appear to be women whose internal secretions are antagonistic to sperm, or at any rate to certain types of sperm, and perhaps others who lack the enzymes which capacitate sperm. By fertilization in the test-tube (scientists use the term *in vitro*, i.e. 'in glassware' in contrast to *in vivo*, i.e. in the living creature), followed by implantation, these obstacles could be overcome and conception made possible.

Secondly, one can imagine that some women who are wholly infertile might wish to achieve maternity by the implantation of a fertilized egg derived from a donor. This possibility has been described as 'prenatal adoption'. It seems probable that a good relationship is more likely to develop between parent and child when the former has gone through the whole process of bearing the child, and when the child has been conditioned from before birth to the mother, than when adoption takes place some months after birth. Apart from the psychological aspect, there is probably a direct biological basis for this. The young of many species, e.g. sheep, are conditioned to the smell of their mother, and of her alone. To induce a lamb whose mother has died to suckle on another ewe, it is necessary to tie the fleece of the dead animal on to the living one. The prenatally adopted child will have shared its foster-mother's circulation, and its biochemical make-up will reflect the association.

Thirdly, as we shall see later in the chapter, this technique might greatly simplify the techniques which would make it possible to choose the sex of one's child.

Baby factories?

It is impossible to discuss the question of a baby conceived in a test-tube without raising the question whether one day it may be possible to complete the whole development of the foetus in artificial conditions, thus arriving at the kind of 'baby factory' visualized by Aldous Huxley so prophetically thirty-five years ago.

The early stages do not seem unduly difficult. Dr D. A. T. New, at the Strangeways Laboratory, has for some time been able to maintain mouse embryos in laboratory conditions up to the stage at which the heart starts beating. By this time all the main organs have begun to form. Brain, spinal cord, ears, eyes, gut, kidneys, limbs, head, tail – all are present in some degree. Dr New's method is to dissect out the embryo complete with its yolk-sac placenta, when it is about 2 mm. long, and place it on a clot of blood-plasma with a drop of nutrient solution. (Mice have two placentas; the yolk-sac placenta is derived entirely from their own tissues.) At this stage, though there is a rudimentary heart, there is no brain or spinal cord, just a fold of tissue which will form these structures. In the two days which they survive, the embryos quadruple in length. Then they die.

Probably this is because they depend on simple diffusion to bring in nutrients and remove waste products. They need a placenta joining them to the mother's bloodstream to continue further.

Several groups of scientists in Britain, the U.S. and elsewhere are working on the development of an artificial placenta – the immediate motive generally being to provide a way of aiding prematurely born infants, who are liable to die of 'respiratory distress', i.e. breathing difficulties. At King's College Hospital, London, one such machine has kept a human foetus, born at 26 weeks, alive for five hours, apparently in good shape. In design it is based on the well-known heart-lung machines. The umbilical cord from the foetus passes through a lightly coiled cellulose tube, which bathes it in fluid, and oxygen is bubbled through. If the foetal blood is abnormal in composition – for instance the level of sugar in it may be too low – this can be corrected.

The intermediate stages may, however, prove more difficult to duplicate. In the Department of Experimental Medicine at Cambridge, a team has been developing an artificial placenta, on which pig embryos are maintained. It has taken the scientists five years to understand the way in which gases are exchanged between foetus and environment. They expect it to take twice as long again to examine the exchange of liquids and solids. It is probable that the mother supplies hormones and perhaps other substances to the foetus in her womb, but nothing is known in detail about this. On the other hand, the Russians have hinted at remarkable progress, and Professor P. V. Anokhin of the Academy of Medical Sciences is known to have been working on the problem for many years, though little detailed scientific information has been published.

A considerable technical problem is presented by the transfer of a foetus to an artificial placenta. It is exceedingly difficult to join plastic tubes to the tiny and fragile veins and arteries of a foetus let alone an embryo. Moreover, the blood-cells are easily damaged and seem to be adversely affected by contact with artificial substances. It will almost certainly be necessary to find out how to maintain foetuses from progressively earlier and earlier stages of development before the problem is solved.

But, according to the *New Scientist*, 'The development of the "perfect" artificial placenta can only be a matter of time.' Once it is evolved, the problem of the therapeutic abortion – carried out to protect the health of the mother – will become even more delicate, for she could be protected by transferring her six-week-old foetus to a machine. What, asks the writer, should our attitude be to an unwanted foetus which can be brought to maturity through the agency of a machine?

In Huxley's vision, society's attitude was entirely favourable. The very word mother had become impolite, not to say grotesque. It was hardly ever used, since it recalled the barbarous period when human young were conceived blindly and born in pain and blood, after having weighed down a woman's belly for nine months. Instead, a moving conveyor belt carried the embryo from conception to delivery, in a fully automated baby-factory producing thousands of babies a day. But, as the article already cited observed: 'We are out of the realms of fancy now.' *Brave New World* is on its way. It is already late to begin considering the implications.

Choice of sex

In a mid-term view, it is almost certain that the parents of the future will be able to specify, when they are about to create a new baby, which sex it shall be. No doubt many people will be willing to let nature (i.e. chance) decide for them. But a minority, after bearing several children of the same sex, may feel a desire to include at least one member of the opposite sex in their family, to enlarge their experience. For instance, Professor Jacob Bronowski has several times declared that, having had four daughters and no son, if he knew of a chemical which would ensure that he did not have another daughter, he would use it.

If there were an extensive public demand, of the kind that there is for contraception, with the prospect of large profits for the patenter of a satisfactory device, we should probably have a method already, for the problem is relatively a simple one. Male and female sperm differ slightly but definitely, and it must be possible, in principle, to exploit this difference to separate them. Russian workers, starting with the belief that the electric charge on male and female sperm was different, attempted to separate rabbit sperm into two groups by electrical methods (electrophoresis), but their results were only partially successful. Attempts to repeat the work elsewhere were also not too satisfactory. In Sweden, Lindahl tried to exploit the difference in mass by spinning bullsperm in a centrifuge, and achieved the birth of 11 consecutive bull calves. These results need repeating on a larger scale.

Such demand as there is for a method of sex determination comes from animal breeders, who would like to ensure females of the species, since these can now be fertilized by artificial insemination.

The main social issue arising from achieving success in this work would be: would there be a shift in the normal balance between the sexes? By an elegant mechanism, nature ensures that the sexes are equal in number, not at birth, but at the reproductive age. Since males are slightly less liable to survive than females, this means a slight excess of male births. Obviously, in any monogamous society, any serious excess of one sex over the other would create difficulties. Indeed, history shows that, when women outnumber men, polygamy in one form or another is generally permitted. It may be that in western societies there would be some slight preference for a son, expressed perhaps as a tendency on the part of some people to have sons only, more often than daughters only. I suspect that this tendency would not be so marked that it could not be checked by propaganda and good sense. The danger would be, rather, that the public would respond too well, so that the ratio would swing in the opposite direction, only to undergo a further correction. The longer the timelag in detecting a tendency to go out of balance, the greater the likelihood of such a 'hunting' process. Sociologists will therefore need to develop more effective methods of monitoring changes in public behaviour in this respect.

However, it may not be necessary to rely on separating spermatozoa, for it is already possible to alter sex during pregnancy, as the following experiment shows. Dr F. Neumann and Dr M. Kramer of the Schering Co. in Berlin treated pregnant rats with a substance known as cypro-terone acetate, injecting it between the thirteenth and twenty-second days of pregnancy. The male offspring of these rats were born with vaginas. Soon after birth, they were castrated and ovaries were implanted. Later study showed that the implanted ovaries produced eggs in the normal manner and also secreted the hormones which give the female sexual expression its cyclic character. These rats behaved as if they were females and were treated as such by ordinary male rats. Furthermore, very similar results were attained by treating the male offspring with cyproterone acetate immediately after they were born.

It seems almost certain, now, that the brain tissue of the embryo is fundamentally female; male development occurs when the male hormone, testosterone, is manufactured on instructions from the male chromosome. Cyproterone acetate neutralizes the effect of the testosterone. It may be, therefore, that it will be easier to turn boys into girls than girls into boys. This may have some advantages, since sociologists believe that there will be an increasing tendency for men to outnumber women. More boys than girls are born, but this tends to be corrected by their greater liability to die, as I have just noted, so that the ratio of the sexes tends to become equal at child-bearing age. But medical progress is reducing the excess male mortality, and the tendency to complete families earlier adds to the effect. At the Agricultural Research Council's Unit for Animal Physiology near Cambridge an Indian worker, Dr B. C. Bhattacharya, followed up an observation that peasants in his country preferred to bring cows for insemination towards sundown, claiming that this resulted in more male offspring. Bhattacharya reasoned that the two types of sperm might drift downward in the storage containers at different rates – the slightly heavier female-determined sperm sedimenting faster than the male. His sedi-mentation experiments, which have also been tried in Germany, have not yet produced any clear-cut results.

However, the problem is not insoluble – since there is a difference be-tween the two kinds of sperm, it is just a matter of time until someone finds how to exert some leverage on it, and Professor Parkes, one of the world's leading authorities on reproductive physiology, has gone on record as saying: 'There can be no doubt that this technical problem, too, will be solved in time.'

What may well make the whole thing simpler is Dr Edwards's method of *in vitro* fertilization, already described. This makes it un-necessary to separate large quantitites of male and female sperm, as would be necessary if artificial insemination were in view. In the test-tube quite small amounts can be used, since if conception does not occur im-mediately the attempt can be continued as long as necessary. And even if separation were to prove impracticable, it would be possible, using *in vitro* fertilization, to allow a number of eggs to develop to a stage at which the sex of each organism could be determined. Those of the unwanted sex could then be jettisoned, and one of the desired sex implanted. Rather as with a litter of kittens, one could keep the boys and throw the girls away, but long before birth. Farmers will certainly be doing this before long, says Dr Richard Keynes, the Director of the Institute of Animal Physiology.

Obviously, the use of such a procedure in human beings raises in acute form questions of the sanctity of life. In the broad human sense, nothing has been lost: a person who wished to procreate has done so. In a narrow sense, thousands, even millions of potential organisms have been sacrificed. It cannot be said that this is against 'natural law', for this is precisely the method nature employs. Four out of every five birds which are hatched in the wild state are dead within six months. Nature provides a vast excess to balance out the risks of failure. If science eliminates the risks of failure, the excess becomes an embarrassment.

Professor A. S. Parkes takes the view that conception has not occurred until the egg has embedded itself in the lining of the womb, since without this step development cannot occur. If this view is accepted, the problem, of course, vanishes.

It might be argued that to go to such extremes to satisfy one's desire for a child of a particular sex was 'unnatural' – but, alas for this argument, there are often valid reasons for such a policy. Certain types of hereditary disease could be bred out of the population for ever. These include hemophilia, or bleeding, and such rare but damaging diseases as irider-emia, in which the eye lacks an iris. This possibility arises because these diseases are 'sex-linked' – that is, the factor (gene) which evokes them is associated with the factor which causes maleness. Thus in hemophilia, though a woman may carry the defective gene, the disease is only ex-pressed in men. If such women confined themselves to male offspring, this defect could quickly be bred out of the population for ever. We shall discuss the point again in the next chapter.

Commenting on this, the *New Scientist* said:

> This makes good, cold scientific sense. At the same time it exemplifies the manner in which biologists are now replacing physicists as purveyors of the kind of knowledge which could change the nature of life on earth. But Dr Edwards's plan takes no account of those 'bench' embryos not selected for survival. Would their destruction by the laboratory attendant who cleaned up after a day's work amount to an act of abortion? And if it does become possible to choose which of a vast surplus of embryos should be allowed to live and develop, who is to make the choice? Who comprehends all the circumstances which should guide such a choice, even if the principle could be accepted by a public opinion based upon a new and wholly altered scale of values? Who is to say how many girls there should be and how many boys?

Hormonal implications

Many of these new techniques, like others which I shall describe in a moment, reflect the biologists' growing understanding of the whole process of procreation. Though human spermatozoa were first seen under the primitive microscopes of the Dutch draper, van Leeuwenhoek, their function was not grasped: many people thought they were there simply to prevent the fluid coagulating, and even the eighteenth-century Abbé Spallanzani thought it was the seminal fluid, not the spermatozoa, which effected conception. Others believed they were some kind of organism, and vowed they had seen them copulating. It was not until 1856, little more than a century ago, that a German biologist named Pringsheim actually saw a spermatozoon (strictly speaking, it is a spermatozoid) enter the egg-cell of an alga known as *Oedogonium*, and finally removed all doubt about what occurred. In human beings, where the difficulties of observing such an event are obvious, the moment of fertilization was not photographed until shortly after World War II.

Many details still remain obscure. Some I have already noted, such as capacitation. But the basic mechanism is well understood, and also the system of chemical controls by which it is regulated. The brain releases chemical messengers of several kinds which stimulate the reproductive organs, while the organs themselves also release messengers, some of which influence the brain, while others prepare surrounding tissues for roles they must soon fulfil – or one messenger may do both. Collectively, they are known as hormones.

It has become clear that the system of hormonal control which regulates the basically simple process of sperm-meets-egg is remarkably subtle and intricate.

It is these chemical messengers which release the egg, regulate its passage to the womb, control its nesting in the wall of the womb, change the vaginal secretions, and even set the level of desire. The body contains hundreds, or possibly thousands of these messenger substances, other of which regulate a variety of functions from heart-rate to digestion. Since the discovery of the first in the early years of the century, hormone science has become a vast field, and increasing knowledge of their structure and functioning, together with the power to synthesize variants, is giving man the power to intervene in much subtler ways than was possible hitherto, in the working of the human body. The day when growth and develop-ment can be controlled, as an orchestra is controlled by a conductor, is in prospect. The regulation of sexual processes is already possible.

Man's new-won knowledge of hormonal systems is yielding many other results, including control of menstruation, the change of life and of sexual desire. We already have available hormone therapies for women who have reached the menopause – the stage of life at which the ovaries become inactive and cease to secrete the hormones which subserve sexual activity. Thanks to such therapy, women can not only escape the physical symptoms of tension and ill-being that often accompany the menopause, but can also preserve an unimpaired sexuality indefinitely. Rumours that this treatment entailed a risk of cancer are quite unsupported by the facts. Indeed in some cases existing tumours have vanished under the treat-ment.

No doubt it will become possible, if desired, to stimulate the quiescent ovaries, since the number of egg-cells they contain is more than adequate. But owing to the increasing risks of the offspring being defective, and in particular the rising risk of mongolism in babies born to older women, there seems at present no point in such a development. Implantation of an egg from a younger woman might enable such older women to bear babies, if they wish to, with a lower risk, but at present little is known about how far developmental defects may be produced during pregnancy by the falling-off of other secretions.

Certainly, the power to regulate desire effectively can be expected. The brain centres which mediate libido have been identified, and drugs which will affect them selectively can be confidently expected. And if, as Professor Rostand has said, one will soon be able to buy chastity at the drug-store, so too will one be able to buy desire. The possibility of reliable and powerful aphrodisiacs could well raise social problems, compared with which the LSD-jags of the sixties will be small beer, and some form of control may be very necessary. But control means black markets and racketeering, as has already been demonstrated in other fields.

In sum, then, we must definitely expect scientific research to put the whole field of sexual activity, from desire to procreation, within the area of consciously controlled procedures, as, to a considerable extent, it already has done. The devoted brain-worker, the missionary, the politician, the explorer or astronaut, may choose to switch off the sexual drive completely for shorter or longer periods. The playboy may choose to switch it on continuously. In either case, the production of children need not follow. At the present time, most civilized countries impose on the father of an illegitimate child some obligation to support it. This would seem to be based on two assumptions: first, that the man alone could have avoided conception occurring, and second, that it is the task of the man alone to earn the money on which a household depends. Both assumptions are obsolete. Except perhaps in the case of rape, the conception of an unwanted child is as much the fault of the mother as of the father; and with the advent of 'morning-after' contraceptives, there is no longer any justification for illegitimate or unwanted births.

Apart from this, it seems reasonable to expect a further separation between marriage and sexuality. Rightly or wrongly, premarital sexual experience is already common. At least the decision to marry need no longer be based on shotgun procedures, or on conscience or fear of public opinion.

But, with a growing population problem, the state may come to regard the production of unwanted children as a social crime as it ceases to be a moral one. Reliable contraception brings into realistic prospect the possibility of licensing procreation.

Fertility-control

The widespread acceptance of the contraceptive pill is a portent, from which we can deduce some conclusions about how society will react to the new powers I have been discussing. Not only is it already in wide use in industrialized countries like Britain and the U.S.: more significantly, it is being increasingly used by Catholic countries in South America and by Catholics in Protestant countries. A recent survey showed that 21 per cent of American Roman Catholic women under the age of 45 had used birth-control pills. This means that as soon as a technique is found which does not offend personal taboos and which is convenient, by which people can control some aspect of their lives more effectively, they will adopt that technique regardless of theological or moralistic considerations.

But the 'pill' of today is a mere forerunner of the more sophisticated methods of birth-control which are now under development, which will make the regulation of fertility easier and surer and more precise. And at the same time, it is also becoming possible to increase fertility as well as to reduce or abolish it. Thus we are moving out of the phase of crude 'birth-control' into a new era for which the term 'fertility-control' seems more appropriate.

There are many points at which one can intervene in the process of procreation. The currently used pill works by preventing the release of eggs from the ovary. The menstrual cycle is under the control of two hormones, oestrogen and progesterone. Oestrogen is released in the first half of the cycle, up to the point at which the egg is discharged, and serves to prepare the womb-surface to receive the egg. In the second half progesterone dominates, but if the egg is not fertilized, at the end of two weeks production of progesterone ceases and this causes menstruation, which is a discharge of the womb-coat which had been prepared for the egg. It was therefore an obvious line to try giving doses of oestrogen to bring on menstruation or doses of progesterone to stabilize the second phase of the cycle, so that the next egg would never be released.

This was tried as far back as the mid-thirties, but the natural hormones were inactive when taken by mouth, and injections had to be used. A daily injection was obviously an impracticable method. In 1948, however, a British and an Indian scientist, working at Oxford, devised a method of synthesizing substances similar to the natural hormones which did not lose their effectiveness when taken orally. Dr Gregory Pincus of the Worcester Foundation was quick to see the contraceptive possibilities of the artificial progesterone, and soon after the Oxford team published the details of their method patents were taken out in Mexico and the U.S.

On the first tests, certain difficulties emerged: some women had irregular menstruation or occasional bleeding. It was found that adding a small amount of the oestrogen analogue to the progesterone analogue controlled this.

Also awkward was the fact that some of the early analogues tested showed a tendency to masculinize the women who took them. Pincus tested some 200 analogues on rats and rabbits before settling on norethynodrel for trial in human beings. In some early trials, too, the dose was set too low, and pregnancies resulted. In others, an unsuitable balance of the the two components caused nausea and many of those taking the drug refused to continue with the experiment.

Finally, a large-scale study in Puerto Rico proved that the method was highly effective and reliable, provided the pills were taken as instructed. Early fears that the drug might cause a rise in the incidence of cervical or womb cancer (since oestrogen plays some obscure part in this) were dispelled when it was found that the Puerto Rican women who used the new pill actually had a *lower* cancer rate for these organs than usual. Since then, it has begun to look as if the use of the pill also slows hardening of the arteries, though it is still under suspicion of causing an increase in deaths from a form of blood-clotting, thrombosis.

The time-scale shows how long it may take from the first studies to the practical widespread use of a new contraceptive, in this case about 30 years, but, the way having been made plain, probably the new methods now entering the pipeline will not take so long to emerge.

The need for daily doses is an inconvenience, but pills which can be taken once a month or even once a year are on the way. Harry Rudel, the president of Syntex Pharmaceuticals, a firm which maintains laboratories working in this field, recently prophesied the advent of the 'annual contraceptive'. So far, however, the nearest anyone has come seems to be a contraceptive injection lasting three months. A synthetic hormone analogue known as medroxyprogesterone acetate has been successfully tested on 274 women. No pregnancies occurred, though some women had trouble with bleeding. Longer periods have been achieved with animals, and of course there is a good deal of commercial secrecy in this field. Such pills would be especially useful to women who had borne all the children they wanted.

Some people might prefer a pill which permits menstruation to con-tinue normally, and this is also in view, in the form of a substance known as chlormadinine acetate, which seems to render the mucus in the cervix hostile to sperm. (There is some evidence that this mucus exists to filter out defective and non-motile spermatozoa, and the drug may work by stepping-up this eliminatory role.) In 1966 Dr Elizabeth Connell of New York College's Metropolitan Hospital reported on 312 women who had taken this drug – it must be taken daily. They found less nausea than in the classic type of pill; three women became pregnant, though one of these cases was due to failure to observe the instructions.

Still more useful, as some people might think, is the 'morning-after contraceptive'. Such an effect is possible by attacking the procreative process at a different point: that at which the fertilized egg nests in the wall of the womb, and so makes contact with the mother's blood-supply. In 1966 John McLean Morris and Gertrude Van Wagenen of Yale reported to the American Fertility Society that they had tested a substance, identified as ORF-3858, on rabbits and monkeys which worked in this way, and successfully prevented conception up to six days after mating. (The human egg implants in the womb-lining on the sixth or seventh day from fertilization.) They used the Yale colony of rhesus monkeys, for this animal has a similar menstrual cycle to that of human beings. No mal-formations were caused when it was given during pregnancy.

This substance has not yet been approved for use in human subjects but experiments carried out with a similar substance, the natural hormone dimethylstilboestrol, on human volunteers – including some who had been victims of rape – proved effective in preventing pregnancy.

At the Weizmann Institute, Professor M. C. Shelesnyak has found that antihistamines upset the body's hormonal balance and prevent implantation in rats. As he points out, apart from the 'morning-after' aspect, this approach could lead to a pill which need be taken only once a month. So far, trial in humans has been disappointing.

Since such substances obstruct the development of the fertilized egg, it has been claimed that they are not contraceptives but abortifacients, and thus illegal in many countries. If this is decided to be the case, it would naturally make them unacceptable to Roman Catholics, even if the Catholic attitude to birth control is relaxed. But it has never been quite clear what 'conception' means. The first of the Christian fathers to write on the subject was Tertullian, in the third century; he decided that the male foetus becomes animate forty days after conception, the female not till eighty. His comments were based, in any case, on an inaccurate translation of Exodus *xxi* 22, which actually refers to the punishing of a man who injures a pregnant woman. The early Jews, like the Greeks and Romans, did not in fact oppose abortion.

As already mentioned, Professor A. S. Parkes takes the view that conception cannot be dated from an earlier point than that at which the egg implants in the womb, pointing out that we do not speak of a hen aborting when it lays an egg. However, the controversy which surrounded the introduction of the pill itself, and the bitterness which has attended the British decision, in 1967, to reform the law on abortion, suggest that such pills may arouse considerable controversy. History also indicates that, because of their convenience, they will finally be accepted.

Many women hold that it is unfair that they should have the responsibility of taking the necessary measures, and perhaps undergo some risk in so doing. There is thus some social significance in the development, now quite near, of pill-type contraceptives for men. The first attempt to develop anything on these lines seems to have been in 1957, when the oral contraceptive Enovid was given to a number of men for five months. When the drug was withdrawn, there was a rebound effect, and many of the men displayed a higher than normal sperm-count. This could complicate the ethical issue, since a man could claim that he was making use of contraceptives only in order to be sure of procreating later on. (A similar rebound effect has been observed with some female contraceptives also.)

The primary obstacle to such contraceptives is a man's fear of anything which might impair his fertility, so that this rebound effect could prove of some importance in assuring acceptance of the method. Indeed, the head of the only British university department working on this problem, Dr H. Jackson of Manchester, has suggested that its relative neglect is due to research workers being psychologically inhibited from entering the field, and he argues that progress would be faster if women scientists would take it up.

At present, it must be conceded, many of these drugs which reduce the male's ability to make sperm have undesirable side-effects. Thus Nilevan produce loss of desire and potency, which makes it unacceptable. Another group makes the taker extremely sensitive to drinking alcohol: although the intoxication is not serious in itself, the result is alarming, and rules such drugs out. Nevertheless, it is doubtless only a matter of time until a substance which fills the bill is found. Alternate fertility-control, husband and wife taking turns, may then become approved social practice, in order to minimize the side-effects, or possible consequences of long-term use.

There are many other points of attack – for instance, there are substances which, in some wholly mysterious manner, block the egg while it is still in the oviduct. Or, to take a quite different line, it is possible to regulate the menstrual cycle so as to make the 'rhythm' method more reliable. It is possible to vaccinate women against their husbands' spermatozoa, although animal experiments suggest that the method is not wholly reliable, and may persist through life. It might even make the wife allergic to her husband, which might prove inconvenient. The fact is that we still know relatively little about the procreative process despite the enormous amount of work which has gone into studying it. An inkling of how little we know, and what strange things the third-generation contraceptives may be, is given by the work of Hilda Bruce, a British woman scientist who, when working at the National Institute of Medical Research in London in 1958, happened on an extraordinary finding. She put newly mated female mice in a cage next to one containing a strange male, i.e. not the mouse with which the females had mated. The great majority failed to become pregnant and returned to oestrus as if no mating had taken place. Following this up, she found that simply putting the females in a box which had been soiled by the strange male, or putting in their cages a piece of rag on which the male had slept, was enough to prevent pregnancy. Investigation made it clear that the effect was produced by smell, or at least, by some volatile substance produced by the male which acted on the brain of the female and changed her glandular secretions. No such substance can be traced in the urine or faeces and it is supposed that it rapidly evaporates.

The idea is not a wild one, for substances which affect the reproductive cycle are known in insects, under the name of pheromones; and indeed, mice produce a pheromone which advances the time of oestrus of the female.

So far no one knows whether the 'Bruce effect', as it was christened, operates in humans. The probability is that it does. Experiments of this kind foreshadow the possibility of a contraceptive which could simply be inhaled, perhaps something like the nasal dilators used by hay/fever sufferers.

While it would be optimistic to suppose that a 'contraceptive perfume' is in sight, the discovery reveals how much we have still to learn. What is clear is that we are entering an historically new phase in which the regulation of pregnancy is becoming a commonplace, the only problem being to choose the most convenient method on any given occasion, just as we already choose the most convenient of many methods of travel for a journey.

Conclusion

The new powers in the area of reproductive physiology here outlined may not seem too disruptive in social effect, remarkable as they are technically. Yet each one necessitates some kind of legislative or juridical action. We can see something of what this means by considering the case of artificial insemination (donor), a procedure which is no longer unfamiliar, having been with us for some ten years.

In the United States, although some 150,000 people are believed to have been conceived by means of AID, neither state nor federal laws define the rights of the offspring. And only in New York state has a court ruled that a child thus born is legitimate (Strnad *v.* Strnad, 1948). In other states, case/law seems to hold the child illegitimate, whether the husband consented to the arrangement or not.

In 1967, the first criminal case involving AID (according to *Time*) was heard in a Californian court. A man, who had been divorced three years previously, was charged by the District Attorney in Sonoma County with violating a law which makes wilful non/support of a child a misdemeanour. The child had been born by AID six years previously, with the husband's consent. Moreover, the wife had refused offers, which he had made, of financial help. The court might have taken the view that he was exonerated from his legal obligation by the fact that he was not the biological father of the child. But the judge convicted him, citing the principle that 'all children born in wedlock are presumed the legitimate issue of the marital partners'.

No court has yet tackled the question of inheritance rights – though in many states illegitimate children can inherit only from the mother. Several states have tried to pass appropriate legislation, but have been defeated by religious pressure. Oklahoma's bill to legitimize such children may be the first to do so.

The situation in Britain is just as incoherent.

In contrast with contraception, which was specifically prohibited or limited by law and precept in many areas, the new techniques have one advantage: there are no prohibitions to repeal. It is always more difficult to repeal a law than to pass one. When the first adventurous person decides to store semen or to give birth to a parthenogenetic or inovulated child, he or she will probably go ahead and do so. Whether the police or the church will seek to intervene remains to be seen. When Professor Petrucci of Bologna claimed to be fostering a human foetus *in vitro*, a few years ago, it was reported that the Pope forbade him to continue his experiments. The legislatures will not offer clear rulings until a number of cases have created controversy, and judges and magistrates will hand down inconsistent decisions, depending on their view of the situation or, as some might think, on their unconscious prejudices. Injustice and heartbreak will occur. The sensible course – the drawing up of a clear system of rulings in advance, so that people shall know where they stand – will not be adopted, if history is any guide, except possibly in France and in Communist countries. Others will rely on the ancient policy of 'muddling through'.

But these personal issues are of minor significance compared with the gigantic social problem which birth-control has conjured up: that of deciding at what level we want the world's population, and that of each country, stabilized. This is generally depicted as a unique problem: the outcome of two chance developments, the power to cut death rates and the power to limit birth rates. Actually it is, as we shall see in later chapters, a paradigm of various similar social problems which biological advance is on the way to creating. People's reaction to the population problem is an indication of how they may react to these future problems. Many of them try to deny that there is any problem at all.

The current growth rate of 2 per cent per annum may not sound like much but, had it existed since the time of Christ until now, there would be 20 m. people for every person now living, or 100 people per square foot. If it continues at the present rate for two centuries only, world population will be 150 thousand million. The U.S. National Academy of Sciences produced these statistics in its report on the subject, to hammer home the point that such growth cannot continue indefinitely. We can either stop it deliberately or wait until famine and disease or war or all three do it for us. As the report concluded: 'Either the birth rate of the world must come down, or the death rate must go back up.'

Against this, the opinion of experts who were asked about population expansion and food supplies in the course of an enquiry made by the Rand Corporation was that though, in fifty years or so, new methods of synthesizing food would be evolved, until then the growth of world population would be held back by famine, and would probably reach about 8,000 m. by the end of the century.

It follows that expanding agriculture, even if we could do it fast enough, could only be a stop-gap. In fact, it is impossible to expand it fast enough, for population grows geometrically, whereas agriculture can only be increased arithmetically.

The study of animal populations shows that meteoric rises are followed by disastrous crashes to a much lower figure. Nature arranges this by an internal mechanism. The overcrowding causes loss of fertility in the males and inadequate mothering in the females. Various kinds of neurotic behaviour develop. Among crowded rats, for instance, the young males rove about in aggressive groups, pursuing all females and attacking weaker males without provocation. Such behaviour seems alarmingly reminiscent of the disorders which are affecting western society.

The mathematician Professor Fred Hoyle has pointed out that Malthus was wrong in assuming that starvation would hold the population at the subsistence level, at which everyone had just enough food to remain alive. The evidence is that population levels decline abruptly, until a new rise starts. He has calculated that such a crash is due in A.D. 2250 when, he thinks, world population will have reached 25,000 m. (from the current 3,000 m.). It will fall to about 2,000 m., and the process will repeat itself eve.y 300 years.

That is, if man fails to take the matter in hand – since, for the first time, he has the knowledge which can prevent or control such increases. Hoyle's dead-pan figures tell us that 23,000 m. people will die in each cycle. Those who oppose the planning of conception may have such deaths upon their conscience.

Unfortunately, the east has been slow to foster the growth of family planning – and it is in the east where growth is most rapid. Western efforts to press the point are often regarded with suspicion as motivated by the fear of being outnumbered. Birth-control is seen as the west's secret weapon. Yet studies like those in Tai-chung show that people want to limit their families, but need to be shown how. Taiwan (Formosa) is a densely populated island off the coast of mainland China: about 12 m. people live in an area of 14,000 square miles. With the aid of a U.S. foundation known as the Population Council, the provincial health department of Taiwan launched an enquiry about the end of 1962, designed to find out what the inhabitants felt about family planning. Did they want it, and if so, how could they best be helped? Nearly 2,500 women in the city of Tai-chung were interviewed: it was soon evident that, as a group, they were having more children than they wanted and were trying – ineffectively – to limit the size of their families. More than 90 per cent felt this way, but they had very little idea how to go about it, and knew little of their own physiology. They said their husbands felt the same way. (Subsequently, varying methods of instruction were tried out, to find which would be most effective, and the programme is being extended to other areas.) 'If, throughout the world, unwanted children were not conceived, a large part of the population problem would disappear,' was how the Vice-Chairman of the Population Council, one of the organizers of the scheme, summed it up.

The change which we are seeing is the birth of population control as a normal function of government. To decide what is an optimum population level for human happiness and fulfilment is a task which the social sciences have not yet faced up to. The political ambitions of some nations and some religious groups are expressed in the form of a desire to have the largest possible population, or at least a larger one than anyone else. Such a drive was formerly little more than a desire to have as many soldiers as possible. However, with the mechanization and automation of war, quality may become more important than quantity, and a large population in relation to land area may become a handicap: hard to feed and still harder to protect from nuclear weapons and fall-out. The day may be approaching when dictators will find their will-to-power best served by having the smallest possible population, provided it is a skilled, intelligent élite.

Man's reluctance to admit the reality of his new social responsibilities is matched by his reluctance to see that the changes in his personal life are of a radical character. If *Homo faber* – man the engineer – was a new species, then *Homo biologicus* – man the master of his biological characters – must also be regarded as a new species. Professor Jean Rostand has dramatized the biological novelty of this new man by describing its characteristics: a strange biped that will combine the properties of self-reproduction without males, like the greenfly: of fertilizing his female at long distances like the nautiloid mollusc; of changing sex like the xiphophores; of growing from cuttings like the earthworm; of replacing its missing parts like the newt; of developing outside its mother's body like the kangaroo and of hibernating like the hedgehog.

And, as the next chapters will show, even this list by no means exhausts the novel capacities promised by current biological research.

3

The Modified Man

In 1952, a young American, identified as Mr R. H., began to notice some puffiness in his feet and legs. He was doing his military service, and the army doctors then discovered, what had not been observed during his physical examination on induction into the Army, that his blood pressure was unduly high and his urine abnormal. It was clear that he was suffering from chronic renal failure, in short, kidney disease, and that his condition was getting rapidly worse. He was 22.

He had had scarlet fever when he was only five. This was before the discovery of penicillin made it possible to control streptococcal infections, and they were liable to cause acute kidney disease.

During 1952 and 1953 he received treatment at the Boston Public Health Service Hospital, but his condition grew progressively worse. In the fall of 1954, learning that he had a twin brother, his doctors began to consider whether an operation to transplant a kidney from the healthy twin to the sick one would be feasible. Up to this point, though transplant operations had been performed on several patients, they had never been successful. As early as 1950 French doctors had removed kidneys from guillotined criminals and implanted them into uraemic patients; the following year British and American surgeons essayed the task, often with kidneys taken from hydrocephalic children. The surgery was satisfactory, and for a few days the implanted kidney would work well. Then there would be a 'rejection crisis'. The bodily defences, which exist to deal with invaders, and which, as many people know, cause skin grafts to be sloughed off, would seek to dispose of the implanted kidney. The best results achieved had been a survival time of a few months, but more often it was only a few days. But it was known that skin grafts could be exchanged between identical twins. Perhaps a kidney transplant would survive in such a case too.

The first step was to make sure that Mr R. H.'s brother was genuinely an identical, or one-egg, twin and not just a fraternal twin. (Each had an identical birthmark on the ear, and their blood-groups were identical. Skin grafts were exchanged to settle the point.) It was also necessary to be sure that his own kidneys were both free from disease, and that there was no reason to suppose that he might develop kidney disease later in his one remaining kidney. Mr R. H. had also to be studied closely.

Now the surgeons and doctors had to face the moral and ethical problem: was it right to take a kidney from a normal person to rescue another who was ill and likely to die? The twin himself was positive that he wanted to help his brother in this way, and the team decided to go ahead. The operation was performed two days before Christmas – 23 December 1954. Dr J. Hartwell Harrison removed the left kidney from the donor in one operating room, while Dr Joseph E. Murray dissected out the blood vessels of the diseased kidney in the operating room next door. The kidney was without a blood supply for one and a half hours while the transfer was made and the veins and arteries were joined up. As soon as this was done, and before even the ureter, or urine-duct, had been joined to the bladder, 'drops of crystal-clear normal urine could be seen coming from the divided end of the ureter.' The two diseased kidneys were not removed.

After the operation Mr R. H. recovered rapidly. His heart, which had been enlarged, returned to normal; his appetite and strength improved, his urine became normal. He was on the road to convalescence – but for one thing. His blood pressure was not falling as fast as had been hoped. It was judged that this was due to the presence of the two diseased kidneys. These were therefore removed, with good results. Mr R. H. was dis-charged from hospital, married the nurse who had looked after him in hospital, and began to raise a family.

This was an historic event. For the first time, real hope of aiding sufferers from kidney disease dawned. True, identical twins comprise only 1 in every 270 births, so that the numbers of people who could immediately be helped was still small. Nevertheless, this was real progress, and by the fall of 1963 some 30 transplants in twins had been performed throughout the world. Not all were as successful as the case just described.

Experience revealed various snags: for instance, some people's kidneys are supplied with blood by two small arteries of unequal length, instead of one large one. But the main doubt – that the new kidney would succumb to an infection – had been removed. Unfortunately, however, it also emerged that the implanted kidney was liable to develop the original disease. Mr R. H. died of nephritis eight years after his operation.

But the operation was historic in a far wider sense also, for it marked the dawn of a new era in surgery – transplantation surgery. Suddenly, it became possible to look forward to the day when not only kidneys, but hearts, lungs, livers, limbs and any other organs you care to mention could be transplanted. That day could dawn tomorrow. As this chapter will show, extensive powers of transplantation will not only make a much greater difference to human welfare and human life than might at first be supposed; they will also create severe ethical and technical problems in the supply of the required organs.

As long ago as the sixteenth century surgeons dreamed of transplantation surgery; Gaspare Tagliacozzi described his attempts to replace noses, lips and ears and there are even earlier instances. But these replacements eventually died and sloughed off. To replace major organs, such as kidneys or lungs, was of course beyond the surgical competence of these early surgeons, but in the mid-1890's Alexis Carrel perfected techniques of joining blood vessels, believing that, since antiseptic methods were understood, the permanent transplantation of tissues and organs would follow. When he found his implants were rejected, he abandoned the effort in despair.

The mechanisms which underlie graft rejection turn out to be remarkably complicated and probably serve other purposes as well. When the body is being formed in the embryonic stage, cells of different types seem to recognize one another and to link up with their own kind, thus forming tissues. Recognition probably depends on the presence of some pattern on the cell-surface – perhaps a pattern of electric charges – too subtle for our present instruments to detect, let alone analyse. It is probably the same power of recognition which enables the body to identify invading bacteria or grafted tissue as 'foreign' and to set in operation the scavenging systems which destroy the strange cells. A great deal of work is being devoted to immunology, as the study of these processes is called, and a final understanding will doubtless affect many fields beside tissue transplantation.

In the meantime, there are some rule-of-thumb methods which offer chances of success. The first is to use X-rays or special drugs which will knock the immune mechanisms out of action. The main disadvantage is that they also leave the patient wide open to infection by bacteria, and costly germ-free surgical units are required if the risk of the patient dying of some common infectious disease is to be avoided. In addition, these violent methods are liable to damage other body mechanisms and so reduce the patient to a low state in which recovery is even more chancy. Both size and timing of dose are critical. The use of X-rays *and* immuno-suppressive drugs has also been tried. This makes possible a smaller dose of each than if it were the only method used, and so reduces the side-effects.

When an organ is implanted, at first it generally 'takes' all right. But as the body mobilizes its defences, there is a 'rejection crisis'. If, thanks to immunosuppressive treatments, the body fails to reject the implant, things quiet down and the organ probably takes, though sometimes there is a second 'rejection crisis' a few weeks later. The first operation using X-rays to knock out the defence system was attempted in 1958; the first using an immunosuppressive drug (azathioprene) in 1961. In the latter case, the kidney took despite two 'rejection crises' but the patient survived only 36 days owing to the toxic effects of the drug. In the case of X-rays the margin between a lethal dose and one which will knock out the defences long enough for the kidney to 'take' is also an extremely narrow one.

Recently, a more promising approach has been developed, known as tissue-typing. This starts from the well-known fact that people cannot accept transfusions of blood from any donor, but can only accept compatible types. This is simply another, though rather simpler, aspect of the immune story. It led to the thought that perhaps tissues also comprise a number of types, so that people could accept a graft from a donor of the same type, but would reject one from a donor of different type. (Or, as with blood, the story might be a little more complicated, some types being acceptable to everyone, others being acceptable to a limited range of groups, yet others mixing with their own type alone.) Work by L. Brent and P. Medawar at the National Institute of Medical Research in London has recently demonstrated that there is, indeed, a wide range of tissue types of varying compatibility. This undoubtedly explains why surgeons, when doing grafts between people other than twins, have had such variable results, and perhaps why rejection crises vary so widely in severity.

Work proceeds on developing tissue-typing techniques for man – Brent and Medawar's work was done on rats – and may well bring about a breakthrough in transplantation surgery well before the whole story of the immune response is understood. According to Dr J. W. Streilin of the School of Medicine at Pennsylvania University, we are 'on the verge of success' in this area, while 'at least an interim solution of the problem will soon be available'. There are also other lines of approach under study: for instance, it has recently been shown that the thymus gland – a pear-shaped structure at the base of the neck – is responsible for manufacturing the 'antibodies' which bring about graft rejection. Animal experiments show that removal of the thymus abolishes the immune response.

It might be added that the immune response is even sharper when a graft is made from an animal of one species to one of another – for instance, from a pig to man. The body says, in effect, 'Hey, this is not only not me – it isn't even human.' Since, as we shall see, the possibility of taking organs from animals to replace damaged human organs is a serious one, the point is important.

In fact, thanks to immunosuppressive drugs, the first kidney transplant from an animal to man was made by Dr K. Reemtsma of Tulane University Medical School – no suitable human donors being available – in 1964. Both kidneys were transplanted and functioned well, despite two rejection crises, though the patient only survived eight weeks, unfortunately.

It is worth looking back for a moment to see how this new field has developed, since this gives us some insight into the accelerating rate of biological advance.

It was in the late 1920's that two American workers, Dr Padgett of Kansas and Dr Brown of St Louis, showed that skin could be successfully transplanted between identical twins. At the time this seemed just an oddity, and the implication – that rejection need not always occur – was not fully realized. The discovery which really started people looking at the subject seriously was made during the war. Gibson and Medawar, working on the problem of grafting skin on to burned RAF pilots in 1942, showed that giving a man a skin graft makes him abnormally sensitive to grafts of other organs from the same donor. To the layman this might only seem to make the picture darker, but to the scientist it revealed that the immune response could be regulated. If it could be turned up, presumably it could also be turned down. Up to now, no one had known there was a control. After the war was over, work was intensified, leading to the achievements already described:

1942 first insight into problem
1950 first unsuccessful kidney transplants
1954 first successful graft between identical twins
1958 first successful graft between non-twins
1964 first animal-to-man graft

Today there are hundreds of patients who have survived at least one year after the operation, many who have survived three and a very few who have survived for five or more. If it has taken twenty-five years to achieve this much, what will the next twenty-five years bring? A wide range of possible operations is seriously being explored by surgeons.

Transplantation possibilities

Operations for transplanting organs have so far been largely confined to the kidney, partly because most people have two kidneys and can spare one, partly because the surgery is not as difficult as in the case of some other organs. However, surgeons have not been slow to study the surgery of transplanting other organs. Normally they work with dogs, since the blood-vessels are inconveniently small in smaller animals and since monkeys and apes are costly and hard to get. The usual approach is to remove the organ under study, wash it out, and then reimplant it in the same animal, thus avoiding the purely immunological problems. (This is known as an autograft.)

By these experiments, the purely surgical problems of connecting up lungs, liver and even hearts have been largely solved, although difficulty is often met in avoiding blood-clotting. Removal of the liver, in particular, seems to lead to some derangement of clotting mechanisms. Nevertheless, some operations have even been attempted in man. Thus at the Veterans Administration Hospital in Denver, Dr T. E. Starzl performed three liver implantations, the longest survival time being 22 days. Later, he reported that a dog had survived for seven months with an implanted liver, thanks to use of an immunosuppressive drug, and was still all right at the time of his report. At the end of 1967, a survival time of 45 days was claimed as the 'best yet' in a human being – in this instance, a one-year-old baby.

Unfortunately, the liver is more sensitive to damage when deprived of its blood supply than the kidney, and the fact that the patient's own liver must be removed first (unless the new liver is placed in an unusual site) adds to the operative risk.

The first human lung implantation took place in 1963, in Jackson, Mississippi, when Dr J. D. Hardy performed on a man who also had chronic kidney disease. The patient died of the kidney trouble 18 days later, but the lung had been accepted. This was seen as encouraging, for little was known about the immunological sensitivity of the lung. So there now seems a good hope of being able to treat the disease known as chronic pulmonary insufficiency, a condition which menaces teenagers as well as adults.

The transplant operation which would certainly have the most widespread effect on the human condition is the replacement of a damaged heart. As I write, the first such operations are being performed: whether the patients will tolerate the graft for a worthwhile period remains to be seen. Surgically, the operation is not unduly difficult – some surgeons like to transplant heart and lungs simultaneously, which reduces the number of vessels to be connected – but the rejection problem is particularly severe, since even a few minutes of defective action could starve the brain of oxygen and damage it irreversibly. Unless there were warning, it is unlikely that a heart-lung machine could be connected to the patient quickly enough to save him and perhaps tide him over the crisis.

But if such heart transplants prove feasible, the demand for replacement hearts will immediately be enormous: heart disease is western man's biggest killer. The supply is unlikely to be adequate: only the hearts of healthy youngish persons dying of diseases which do not affect the heart (such as brain tumours) or killed suddenly in accidents are acceptable.

It will doubtless be necessary to organize special methods of collecting suitable hearts and seeing that as few as possible are wasted. Why bury in the ground what co ld give another person life? The moral issue is clear-cut.

For this reason consideration has already been given to the possibility of transplanting animal hearts to humans. But the likelihood of rejection is greater and in the only such operation so far performed the patient died almost immediately.

Less obvious than these, but extremely important, is transplantation of the intestine. This is urgently needed for cases where the intestine has been injured by shot or other wounds, or by blood-clotting. Since we all have 20 feet or more of intestine, donors could spare three or four feet without inconvenience, and the gift would be 'a positive luxury to the recipient', to quote the words of one well-known surgeon. The surgery is quite awkward, since there are numerous small veins to be joined, but it is well worth study.

The grafting back of lost limbs is obviously of great practical importance, and in 1962 there was a stir about the grafting back of an arm on to a boy named Ev Knowles, living in Somerville, Massachusetts. It had been sliced cleanly off when he was trying to steal a ride on a local goods train. Ev gripped the arm with his good hand, and by luck was got to Massachusetts General Hospital in Boston before he bled to death. And it happened that a surgical team at the hospital had been training itself to attempt just such an operation. The arm was successfully re-attached. In subsequent operations, attempts were made to restore control to the arm and hand by nerve grafts, with partial success. This is the central difficulty. Nerve-cells have lost the power of division and nerves do not regenerate, though a small margin of adaptation may remain. Two years after the accident he had recovered some of his grip.

Limb-grafting dates from 1954, however, when Anastasy G. Lapchinsky of the Research Institute for Experimental Surgical Apparatus and Instruments at Moscow made what was apparently the first successful limb graft on an Alsatian dog. The animal survived for six more years, standing and running on the implanted limb quite happily, despite its being shorter than the others.

Chinese and Japanese surgeons have been active in this field, sewing back both feet and hands and getting at least partial restoration of function.

The way is now open to the first restoration of an entire leg. If immuno-logical problems could be solved, such work might benefit the arthritis sufferer as well as the victim of automobile or industrial accidents, and perhaps even the 'thalidomide' babies and other phocomelic babies lacking normal limbs.

The implantation and transplantation of teeth has been frequently attempted since the time of the great sixteenth-century surgeon, Ambroise Paré, but after two or three years the transplanted teeth fall out. But in the last few years it has been found that the buds from which teeth grow can be transplanted quite successfully and will produce normal teeth. The way therefore seems clear towards providing replacement teeth as soon as banks of teeth-buds can be organized.

Another major area in which transplantation techniques are being worked out is that of the endocrine glands, such as thyroid, parathyroid, pancreas and pituitary. While the thyroid and pancreas do not represent an urgent problem, since patients can be treated quite easily with thyroid extracts and insulin, the implantation of pituitaries is badly needed for children born with acute pituitary insufficiency – as a result of which their growth remains permanently stunted and their whole development, including their sexual development, becomes abnormal. Pituitary extracts are not commercially available.

The surgical problems are straightforward, but the pituitary depends on a special blood supply: blood reaches it after passing through certain cells in the brain, believed to secrete substances into it. It may prove difficult to provide it with blood which has been processed in this way – and without it, who knows whether it will function or even survive?

Some history was made in 1967 when the first pancreas was trans-planted into a diabetic woman of 32 and functioned well. Adults are normally so well sustained by insulin that the risks of operation are prob-ably not worth taking – at present anyway – but when diabetes appears quite early in life, the outlook is much poorer, and operation may be the only means of avoiding a fatal outcome. In this case the patient was in terminal renal failure, with high blood pressure, blind and with kidney-disease complicating the picture. A kidney was also implanted, and she now lives without need of insulin. Dr R. C. Lillehei and W. D. Kelley made the transplantation, after an earlier attempt on another patient, using a somewhat different surgical technique, had failed.

There is one type of organ which deserves special mention: the gonads or sexual organs. A small proportion of women are unable to have babies either because they lack ovaries, or because their ovaries are defective. For them, the implantation of new ovaries, or even ovarian tissue, might restore the power to raise a family. Since the ovary contains the growing points for hundreds of eggs, even a small slice of ovarian tissue would yield enough to meet the needs of the recipient. Following experiments with rats and monkeys, Dr S. H. Sturgis has tried the effect of implanting ovarian tissue contained in small chambers of permeable material. But, although there was some evidence of ovarian stimulation, it was not enough to encourage him to experiment further.

Nevertheless, there is no reason to suppose that such an operation is impossible, or even as difficult as a kidney transplant. The reason for mentioning it is the ethical issue involved: would the children derived from an implanted ovary be regarded in law as the mother's own children, or would they have to be officially adopted, after their birth? A similar problem would naturally arise if testicular implantation were successfully performed on a man.

It is clear, then, that only the difficulties of the immune response are holding up a truly vast extension of the field of transplantation surgery, and it is the purpose of this chapter to outline what such a development might mean for society. But before considering remoter issues let us look at the problems of supply, for these also raise social and ethical problems.

Sources of supply

There are currently three and only three sources from which organs for transplantation can be obtained – although, as I shall describe, the remoter future may see others. The three are: living persons, dead persons and living animals.

From the purely surgical point of view, the living donor is the most desirable source: the organ is in healthy condition and can be transferred with a minimum of delay to the recipient. The cadaver is a less satisfactory source for several reasons. The organ is often harmed in the course of the death agony. Furthermore, it is difficult to ensure that the recipient is present and ready for operation at the moment of death of the donor, so that some delay is almost inevitable, during which the organ deteriorates rapidly. A kidney should be taken within ten minutes of death, and pref-erably within five. Equipment now exists on which a kidney can be kept going for a day or more after removal, but there is also the difficulty of obtaining permission from relatives with sufficient speed.

Animal organs, as already noted, evoke a stronger graft-versus-host reaction and are therefore, at present, less desirable than human organs. But since they are freely available in good condition they may, when the immune response has been overcome, become the first choice, provided they prove to function as effectively in man as they do in their own species. This being so, we need not consider the dead animal as a source, since the organ from a live one is likely to be in better condition.

Of course, there is a further alternative: the provision of man-made imitations of human organs. At present these are generally less satis-factory than the natural models.

A good deal has been heard recently of artificial hearts – and the work of Dr DeBakey of Houston, who succeeded in implanting one – but the heart is a comparatively simple piece of machinery, little more than a double pump. Even so, it is a problem to drive it. No way of powering an artificial heart except by leads from a large power source outside the body has yet been devised. To imitate the liver or the kidney within the same range of size as the real organ, so that the artificial one can be put in its place, is still far beyond human ingenuity. The artificial kidney, though now much smaller than it was, is still much larger than the human kidney and, furthermore, requires to be kept still and level, as well as being provided with an external source of power. Its membranes need frequent replacement.

Artificial livers have not even been attempted. Even skin, which seems to the uninitiated such a simple structure, is actually far too complex to imitate in any real sense. Real skin replaces itself from below when abraded, thickens in response to pressure, increases its supply of sweat-glands when placed in a hot climate, and so on. (Almost the only reason-ably satisfactory replacements at present are arteries, bone-joints and teeth. The use of metal hip joints for people whose joints have been damaged by arthritis is now almost standard practice. Plastic corneas have been attempted, but seem to cause local irritation.)

For the present, therefore, this source can be neglected, although, as noted later, it might eventually become an important rival to trans- plantation, or a supplement to it.

That we entertain the possibility of living donors at all is mainly due to the fact that nature has provided so much reserve kidney capacity that a person can afford to part with one kidney without any measurable loss of kidney function. He suffers no direct handicap from his gift. Like a motorist who gives his friend his spare tyre, he only accepts a slight risk of finding himself in trouble later.

A living donor might also be able to supply small quantities of skin, and perhaps other tissue, such as ovarian or endocrine tissue, or bone. But he could not reasonably be asked to supply a limb, even though limbs are paired, or an eye. Whether he could afford to supply a lung is question- able: there are tuberculosis patients who function pretty well on a single lung, but with advancing age one needs increased lung capacity, and especially if heart defects develop as a result of which the blood is not fully oxygenated.

In any case, there is always a slight but significant operative risk, which includes both the possibility of errors or carelessness in the operating theatre and that of post-operative infection.

On ethical grounds, therefore, it is clear that we must look urgently for other sources of supply. Currently, this means cadavers.

However, most of those who die in hospital are unsuitable as donors. Many are old, or have been ill for a long time, and their organs are in poor shape. If the person concerned had hardening of the arteries, or arteries narrowed by the fatty deposits of atheroma, they may have been starved of blood. It is therefore the victims of accidents, who die soon after arrival in hospital, who provide the main source of supply. Precisely in this kind of case it is difficult to obtain permission of relatives with sufficient speed. Even if they can be located, they are likely to be in a state of shock and anxiety in which it is difficult to consider such a request.

The problem of obtaining organs in good condition would obviously be greatly simplified if organs taken from people at the time of death could be held in storage until needed. Even a storage time of 48 hours would make an enormous difference, as it would permit an intended recipient to be brought into hospital and prepared for the operation as soon as a suitable organ was available. Longer storage times would make it possible to hold a variety of organs of different sizes, or with different arrangements of blood supply, and, above all, of different tissue types. If the time of storage without deterioration could be extended from months to years, it would be possible to build up a reserve against the possibility of a heavy demand after a disaster.

But storage is not, as people often suppose, just a matter of putting organs into a refrigerator or deep-freeze. As we shall see in more detail in the next chapter, where the storage of whole bodies is discussed, most tissues are damaged by prolonged exposure to low temperatures. As the water in the cells freezes, the concentration of salts in what remains becomes stronger until it is damaging. Ice crystals may also form and puncture the cell wall. This can be averted to some extent by using special solvents such as glycerol, and other methods, but progress so far is patchy.

The main things which can successfully be stored so far are – in addition to blood – skin, bone and the cornea, or window, of the eye. The storage of skin has been particularly successful: the wonder-solvent known as DMSO, widely used in industry for many years, has proved to be satisfactory in storing skin. In 1965, Dr Ronald Berggren and Herndon B. Lehr of the University of Pennsylvania School of Medicine reported that they had successfully made grafts with human skin which had been stored for periods as long as two years in this medium. Until a suitable medium was found, the task was difficult. Severe freezing destroys skin's ability to survive, while it deteriorates rapidly when merely refrigerated.

When a person loses skin – most often this is the result of burns – skin is taken if possible from some other part of his body, to avoid the risk of its being rejected. (Skin is particularly awkward in this respect.) But the amount which can be taken at any one time is small, for large denuded areas do not cover themselves with skin, but simply form scar tissue. This means a series of operations. The same is true, of course, when a donor gives skin, and the recipient has to undergo surgery every time the donor donates. But with storage, the donor's skin can be accumulated and applied to the recipient in a single operation, greatly speeding his recovery and reducing risk.

The technique of storage is being steadily improved. For instance, it has recently been found that cobalt irradiation after freezing improves the keeping qualities of bone. The first tissue bank in the U.S. was established as long ago as 1949 at the Navy's medical headquarters in Bethesda, Maryland, to meet the needs of war-wounded. Using freeze-drying techniques (in which the water is removed from the tissue by sublimation) red blood-cells have been stored for years, while bone stored for as much as eleven years has successfully been used. In 1961 it supplied 3,000 square inches of skin to Brazilian hospitals, after large numbers of people had received major burns in a large fire. In the next few years we are bound to see the establishment of increasing numbers of such storage banks, and the inclusion of a much wider range of organs in them. Methods of transporting stored organs to disaster areas will need to be developed.

While organ storage will probably be the main source of supply for 'spare-part' operations in the next fifty years or so, beyond that we can expect to see a far more radical alternative: the growing of organs from embryonic tissue, in whatever quantities required. The maintaining of cells and tissues in culture is now a well-developed technique, the first steps in which were taken more than half a century ago by an American, Ross Harrison, who maintained nerve cells alive in isolation. Since the war, notably at the Strangeways Laboratory in England, a start was made on maintaining organs. First, small thigh bones, taken from an embryo, were grown to many times their initial size. More recently, in Paris, Etienne Wolf at the Collège de France has grown embryonic tissue destined to become not only bone but skin and testis; he has even been able to change the sex of the gonadal tissue by the application of hormones. He is now working on the growing of eyes.

The more complex the organ to be grown, the harder the task. As size increases it becomes harder to remove the products of metabolism, and to ensure a supply of raw materials. At the appropriate stage of development, a blood supply will have to be provided, just as it is in life, and this blood will have to carry all the nutrients and perhaps the control substances which are found in the appropriate maternal blood. But the problem is simply a technical one: it may prove tricky to solve, but that it is soluble in principle is not in doubt.

Later still, I fancy, there may be no need to rely on embryos for the starting material. We may well solve the problem of inducing organs to regenerate of their own accord. Alternatively, transplantation may be replaced by autoplantation. It is now known for certain that every cell in the body of any organism carries all the information needed to construct whole organs or indeed the body itself, as Professor Steward's work, already described, shows. If geneticists can discover how to release this information in a controlled manner, we could simply take a few cells from any part of a sick man, and grow duplicates of his defective organs from them. Transplantation will become unnecessary.

One day, therefore, we may expect to see 'organ factories', from whose catalogue a surgeon will be able to order a heart, a liver or a pancreas of any desired size and capacity, with the assurance that it will be youthful and in prime condition. Cannibalization will no longer be needed.

The legal and ethical issues which have already arisen in cases of organ transplantation are more numerous and awkward than is generally realized, and it is worth looking at them fairly closely, since this will give us a better idea of the amount of confusion which could be caused by some of the other possibilities described later in this book.

Is it legal?

The history of practical organ transplantation is still a very short one, but the progress which has been made in a dozen years or so is considerable. In addition to success with identical twins, there have been several successful instances of transplants between brothers and at least one between a mother and her son. Not long ago, Dr Joseph E. Murray made a world-wide survey of 374 such operations performed in the previous two years. Leaving aside those cases in which the most modern methods had not been used, he was left with 262 cases; of these 110 of the patients had lived the full two years and were still alive. While this is less than half and obviously unsatisfactory, nevertheless it means that the legal and ethical issues are now far from academic.

In British law, and thus generally speaking in American law, which is derived from it, it is an offence to do anything which makes one unable to serve one's country, to consent to such a thing being done to one, or to do it to another. This law was established in medieval times and such an act is known as a maim. Under it, it was illegal to remove a front tooth, though all right to remove a molar – presumably because one might wish to bite one's enemy! Castration was particularly objected to, as it was thought that this reduced one's courage and aggressiveness. This law governs transplantation.

Today the law is usually interpreted more broadly and exception has of course long been made for surgical operations in the interests of health. But it is by no means clear that it permits a surgeon to injure a healthy person by removing his kidney, or for that person to consent to such an operation. As the eminent jurist Lord Riddell once commented: 'A man may be captain of his soul but he is certainly not master of his body.'

Despite this, surgeons have been extremely careful to obtain consent from intending organ donors and have sometimes consulted the coroner as well. Once such consent has been given the person concerned is estopped from bringing any action himself, whatever the public prosecutor may do. But courts are increasingly insistent that consent shall be based on a genuine understanding of the issues involved, and doctors face difficulties where possible donors are of low intelligence, questionable mental balance or under duress, as in the case of criminals or prisoners.

The problem also becomes awkward when donors under the 'age of consent' are in question and, possibly for the first time in history, an issue of this kind came before an American court in 1956. One of a pair of identical twins, whose age was under 21, came to the hospital with advanced kidney disease; his brother was in excellent health. With the approval of the donor twin and the parents, a psychological study was made. The psychiatrist reported that in view of the close attachment between the boys, the knowledge that he had failed to help his brother when he might have done would heave a 'grave emotional impact' on the healthy twin. In consideration of this, the Massachusetts Supreme Court (Justice Edward A. Counihan, jr.) ruled that the hospital and the surgeons could proceed, given the consent of the parents and the donor, without incurring liability, civil or criminal, for their action. The same court subsequently allowed operations on twins aged 14. Later, similar judgments were made by other courts.

However, when faced with twins under 12, the hospital in question declined to take on the task, on the grounds that the donor was not old enough to understand the possible harm to himself, and so could not give valid consent. Equally, it was thought that he was too young to suffer lasting remorse at not having been permitted to help.

Though legal experts have generally held that an organ may be removed from a living person if permission is given, one cannot legally consent to a public mischief. This became an issue in a British case in which a man had himself sterilized and was subsequently sued by his wife on grounds of cruelty. On appeal, one of the three appeal judges, Lord Denning, held that he had no legal right to have himself sterilized since it was not for the benefit of his health, while the other two judges dissented, and the matter remains uncertain.*

In Italy, this question arose in a different manner. In 1932 a wealthy man induced a Neapolitan boy to sell him one of his testicles for implantation. Public opinion was shocked. In 1940 a law was passed making it illegal to dispose of one's own organs in this way. Quite recently, it was realized that this law made it impossible for anyone to be a kidney donor and a new law had to be introduced to remedy this. Given that it is legal to donate an organ, it is obviously difficult to prevent payment being made for it, or other compensation being offered; a good job, for instance. The recipient of an organ might well feel grateful to the donor and could hardly be prohibited from expressing his gratitude. The law could only prohibit the drawing up of a formal contract, and rule out attempts to recover a defaulted payment.

While Italy has decided against the sale of organs, the case may be different in the U.S.A. where there is a long tradition of paying volunteers. Blood donors are often paid – though it has been argued that this is payment for a service, not a sale. Nevertheless, there are certainly cases where blood *is* bought from agents on a commercial basis. In Britain, as Dr R. Calne, a leading transplantation surgeon, has disclosed, there have been several discreet attempts to buy a kidney.

If a man is to have the power to will the disposal of his body after death, it seems highly inconsistent to say that he has no power to dispose of it in life, and the issue may not be settled everywhere as swiftly as in Italy.

The possibility of a black market also arises. Two years ago, it was reported in *The Times* that in Syria bands of thugs were waylaying travellers and killing them in order to sell their blood and corneas –

* The case of a woman who wishes to be sterilized is also puzzling. Since women now serve in the armed forces, the question of whether sterilization affects her fighting ability might have to be considered! More realistically, a state which was aiming to increase population might make this illegal, where one which was trying to limit population might take the opposite view.

doubtless they lacked the facilities for removing and storing kidneys in good shape.

The donor of a kidney takes on a slight but definite risk that he may one day need that kidney, having himself developed kidney disease. It is already on record that one such donor asked if he would be guaranteed free treatment in such an event. In countries with state medical services, such as Britain, no problem arises, but in the U.S.A., where medical care is costly, the case is very different. At present donors are usually relatives strongly motivated to help a son, or a twin, without consider' ation of reward. When immunosuppression makes everyone a possible donor, as already occurs with blood donations, such powerful motivation will be lacking, though the question of medical care may be secondary to that of compensation. A donor is necessarily absent from work for some weeks, and so suffers financial loss. A woman donor, if she has children and a home to run, may have to pay for help to run her home in her absence. Issues of this kind have not yet been tackled.

A completely different set of issues arises where the surgeon wishes to take an organ from a cadaver.

When Professor Woodruff, one of Britain's leading surgeons in this field, and head of the Wilkie Laboratory for Surgical Research at Edinburgh, set out to establish a skin bank, he found that he was com' mitting an offence under the Anatomy Act of 1832, originally passed to prevent the notorious grave'robbers, Burke and Hare, who supplied corpses to hospitals for anatomical dissection by students, from practising their trade.

It is by no means clear what legal force attaches to a person's declar' ation that he wishes to donate his body for medical research or clinical use. In Britain, the Human Tissue Act, passed in 1961 to remedy the situation just described, represents a retrograde step, since it allows the next'of'kin to overrule a dying person's written declaration that he wishes to dispose of his body or organs to science.

In the U.S. the situation is even less satisfactory, since not only cannot a patient given an irrevocable permit, but permission cannot even legally be sought from relatives before death, still less granted. The situation is usually governed by the Local Coroners Act, or Medical Examiners Act as it is often known. This normally permits the surgeon to make a post'mortem dissection only with the permission of the next'of'kin, except in specified cases such as homicide, suicide and contagion, when it is necessary to determine the cause of death. Moreover, in most states it is illegal to seek permission for such an autopsy, prior to the death of the person concerned. Nor can a patient himself give irrevocable permission for an autopsy: the consent of the next-of-kin must be obtained.

As I have explained, the surgeon has little time – at most a few minutes – to consult next-of-kin and immediately after the death of a relative is often hardly the best moment to raise such a question. Dr Francis D. Moore of Harvard University School of Medicine has spoken out strongly on the subject: 'In seeking the donation of lung, liver, heart, eye or kidney from a recently deceased person, the time-temperature curve begins its inexorable demands the moment circulation has ceased. Every minute spent in seeking permission from each responsible relative, or in telephoning across the country, means another million dead cells.' And he adds, 'Here is a field where we need help from legislators and lawyers, so that previous intent of the patient, his family and his next-of-kin, may remain binding after death.'

In his experience, next-of-kin do give permission freely, so that the delay in consulting them generally worsens the prospects of the recipient to no good end. British surgeons confirm this.

Religious groups sometimes raise objection to using life-saving techniques; in particular Jehovah's Witnesses object to blood-transfusion, on the basis of a fundamentalist interpretation of a passage in *Exodus*, which asserts 'the blood is the life of the man'. Religious objection may perhaps be raised to transplantation, though no case has come to my notice. Surgeons normally respect such scruples; but the situation is different when parents refuse life-saving treatment for a child. On the argument that the state would not allow them to sacrifice their child on an altar, if they proposed to do so for religious reasons (as Abraham was prepared to do with Isaac) efforts are made to over-rule this objection, a common course being – when time permits – to declare the child a ward of the court; the court then permits the requisite transfusion or surgery. But rulings have been made both ways in the U.S.A.

Questions of consent are not the only legal questions to arise.

A particularly interesting case occurred in Britain in 1963, in Newcastle. A man was butted in the course of a fight and fell backwards on his head, causing severe cerebral hemorrhage. Fourteen hours after he was admitted to hospital he ceased breathing and was placed on a respirator. Twenty-four hours later, with his wife's consent, a kidney was removed to be given to another patient. The respirator was disconnected and breathing and circulation ceased. The coroner's court considered whether the removal of the kidney had contributed to his death. On the surgeon's evidence that death was inevitable and that the man had only been placed on the respirator so that the kidney could be removed, the coroner committed the dead man's assailant on a charge of manslaughter.

Here the facts were clear-cut. Future cases may well arise, however, where the jury is not convinced that death was inevitable, and a man's future, even his neck, may depend upon their decision.

In addition to purely legal issues, surgeons have recently been trying to clarify their feelings on issues of an ethical character. Some surgeons, for instance, have refused to take organs from living persons and have relied solely on cadavers, holding that they have not the right, under the Hippocratic Oath, to inflict any damage on the healthy.

Perhaps a commoner issue, however, is their awareness of the moral pressures put upon the donor and the possibility of moral blackmail. One doctor has related how, after he told a possible donor that he was medically unsuitable, he was heard to mutter: 'Now the family can't say I didn't try.' Where the candidate seems unwilling, doctors usually protect him by saying that he was medically unsuitable. Other possible donors may be motivated by a neurotic need for self-sacrifice, and in most cases surgeons insist on a psychiatric examination of the donor.

Apart from what the law may say about consent, a purely ethical problem arises in cases of those under duress. Dr Alex Comfort suggests that criminals might be asked to give up half their liver against a commuted sentence. In 1963, a murderer serving a life sentence was allowed to volunteer to receive a lung in the first lung transplantation ever attempted, at the University of Mississippi Medical Center. The Governor proposed to commute his sentence and seek a full pardon – though this was not held out as an inducement – but after 18 days he died. But this is not quite a parallel case, since he was volunteering to take part in a medical experiment.

Other authorities have been emphatic that criminals should not be asked to donate organs, saying that, even if no reward is offered, the criminal is bound to feel some sense of pressure and to feel that, if he refuses, it will be some kind of black mark against him. Moreover, while in advanced and civilized countries the recourse might be employed with scrupulous care, there is a grave risk that in other countries or where the regime is unscrupulous the practice could be abused, causing serious injustice.

Some may feel a moral issue is posed by taking the organs of animals, though, since large numbers of animals, especially monkeys and chim-panzees, are already reared and slaughtered to provide vaccines, doctors and surgeons are unlikely to regard this as presenting a different moral problem. But the public tends to be less logical. In an emotional sense, to know you carry a monkey's kidney inside you is quite different from taking a shot of polio vaccine, and animal protection societies may attempt to capitalize on this feeling to limit the use of animals for novel purposes, and animal experimentation generally.

In addition to the problems presented by genuine ethical considerations, there are the pseudo-problems created by irrational prejudice, for in-stance racial prejudice. In six Southern states today, as also in South Africa, the blood banks keep separate supplies of 'white' and 'coloured' blood, and there are many whites who would decline a transfusion of the latter. It is therefore likely that such bigots would feel even more strongly about the implantation of a 'coloured' kidney and still more of a 'coloured' heart. It will be a major embarrassment if the organ banks have to keep duplicate supplies of white and coloured organs.

Surgeons themselves feel a greater sense of strain than this account may suggest. 'We cannot understand the law,' Dr Calne has com-plained. 'As the technical decisions become easier, the moral decisions become more significant,' Dr Hamburger, the leading French transplan-tation surgeon, has pointed out. According to Dr Murray, 'This is a new era with a new set of problems.' One thing is quite clear: these new technical powers demand more of the doctor as a man, as well as a surgeon. Superhuman wisdom and patience, insight and sympathy are needed by him who would wield superhuman powers.

Religion likewise faces a challenge, and may not be able to take as long to work out an attitude as it has done in the case of contraception. Vacillation can only bring a further loss of authority; respect can be won only by a prompt and appropriate lead. And if this is the case in the specialized field of transplantation surgery, we can be sure it will be equally true in the coming fields of age-prevention and mood-control described in the chapters which follow.

But so far we have discussed only the most obvious medical applications of this research – the uses which are already virtually with us. But a little further ahead, there are much more startling possibilities.

In the crystal ball

A decisive breakthrough on the transplantation front, such as would certainly follow the discovery of a thoroughly effective method of immuno-suppression, would lead to an expansion of demand so vast that the mind boggles: no preparations are yet being made to cushion the shock.

First among the potential candidates for transplantation surgery are the majority of those who have been maimed or wounded in car or aircraft crashes, in industrial mishaps, and even in the home – to say nothing of those injured in warfare. When we recall that, in the U.S.A., injuries involving temporary total impairment run at almost 10 million a year, in addition to 400,000 impairments for life, it can be seen the demand could be fantastic. To these we can no doubt add many of the 100,000 who at present die from injuries.

Secondly, there are the medical cases. The major cardiovascular-renal diseases alone account for around a million deaths a year. Even if only ten per cent were suitable for transplantation surgery, the demand would be out of all proportion to any facilities available or envisaged. Such a figure is probably far too low, and Professor Woodruff has said he considers the potential demand for lung and liver transplants to be high, 'and for hearts, very high'.

But the man with myocardial infarct would be well advised to replace his coked-up organ before it actually goes 'on the blink' – especially in view of the possibility of irreversible cerebral damage in such a case. I think, in fact, that we may see the emergence of 'prophylactic transplan-tation', that is, transplantation carried out with a view to preventing disease rather than curing it, just as we replace tyres before they actually give way.

Thus transplantation surgery may become a weapon in the war against old age, with routine replacement of organs after a certain number of years' use. Artificial organs may also be implanted for this purpose. It must be added, however, that a leading British gerontologist, Dr Alex Comfort, disagrees, saying that the prospect of repairing age-changes by prosthetics is 'genuinely over-rated', since 'ageing is commonly a general loss of vigour in which certain organs lead'. We cannot renew the whole system, and new organs – like new capacitors in an old radio – might just destroy other ageing components, he considers.

Nevertheless, the man with heart-disease is unlikely to recoil from an operation which could save his life just because he might have trouble with some other organ a year later. Even one more year of normal life is, for most people, worth having. Therefore a secondary consequence of the use of transplantation surgery to prolong life may be an increased demand for the kind of facilities needed by the old.

To these great categories of medically rewarding operations, we can add a range of less urgent demands which could become important as facilities expand. Thus the implantation of ovarian and testicular tissue is obviously likely to be wanted, provided a genuine restoration of sexual function can be shown to follow. There is also likely to be an increased demand for cosmetic surgery, at present limited by the need to take tissue from another part of the same body. For instance, it is currently difficult to reshape ears except in a minor way. In the future, you may be able to pick out the exact pair of ears you want from a tissue bank – a sort of medical supermarket. It is already the case that a number of women think it worth paying for cosmetic surgery of the breasts, and, since suitable tissue is not available, silicone implants are generally used. (One night club singer was recently reported to have greatly increased her income follow-ing the expansion of her chest measurement to 44 inches by this means.) But the implantation of foreign material is always attended with the risk of unfavourable body reactions, or the implanted material may be absorbed and destroyed. The implantation of natural breasts may therefore prove preferable.

Other possible demands can easily be imagined, e.g. for sex-change surgery.

But in addition to these three obvious areas of demand – disease, accident and cosmetics – there are others of a more bizarre character. The obvious end-point to which such a trend leads is the total recon-struction of the human body. Given a trunk to start with, arms could be added from one cadaver, legs from another, liver from a third, kidneys from a fourth and so on. Quite possibly in time of war, a military power might find it worth 'cannibalizing' soldiers, just as in World War II, in North Africa particularly, tanks and trucks were cannibalized. The costs of such multiple operations would normally be prohibitive, but in conditions where the supply of new manpower was difficult, the effort might become worth while; and if the case of the ordinary soldier might be rare it might well be thought worth while in the case of a man of unique intelligence, skill or knowledge. Looking far into the future, one can imagine that a colony of earth-men on a remote planet, receiving supplies from earth only rarely, and these perhaps being delayed by mishap in space, might wish to keep a specialist alive and functioning, and might even think it worth while sacrificing one or two ordinary men to make this possible, somewhat in the spirit of those travellers who, when pursued by wolves, drew lots to see who should be sacrificed to them in order to improve the chances of escape of the rest of the party.

Yet if human cannibalization is likely to be rare, for obvious ethical reasons, no such barrier exists in the case of animals. The experiment of transferring human limbs to an animal may well be tried. If, as I describe later, means of raising the intelligence of apes and other animals are found, there may be a powerful demand for them as slaves, capable of performing simple tasks – this is, after all, only a trifling extension of the practice of using horses to carry men or turn a mill. But for the tasks of a technological civilization, hands with fingers which can press buttons are required, and an opposable thumb is needed for many types of operation. It would therefore be logical to equip apes with discarded human hands. And if lower orders of animals, such as dogs, are also found suitable for such tasks, human arms and even legs may be needed for them.

Up to now, surgeons seem to have avoided transplanting human organs to animals, no doubt from fear of arousing adverse public opinion as much as from difficulties in obtaining permission to use human organs in this way. Nevertheless, there is something to be learned about the mechanisms of immune response from such operations, especially since the immune systems of lower animals seem to be less complex and discriminating than human systems. Were there any commercial or agricultural advantage in having, say, a monkey with a human hand, it would no doubt be done. It would be scientifically interesting to know whether a monkey's brain could make good use of man's opposable thumb, and the time may well come when intelligent monkeys, whose brains have been up/graded by techniques I shall describe in a later chapter, will be used for industrial purposes, space exploration, or maybe to enter radioactive areas to switch off equipment, after a disaster. In this case, the provision of human hands might be an advantage.

The ultimate phase will be cross/species cannibalization: the attach/ment of simian arms and a dog's head to a kangaroo, for instance, might create a creature capable of covering huge distances fast and doing a skilled job when it gets there. And if it is true that dolphins are of almost human intelligence, they might welcome the acquisition of supernumer/ary hands. For of course one need not stop at the conventional ration of two arms and two legs per body. Subject to the limitations of the human frame and its organs, one can vary the picture: dogs with two heads have already been created in Russia some time ago. For an athlete a supple/mentary heart might well be useful, and anyone who has tried to solder two pieces of wire together will have discovered the need for two pairs of hands – an advantage often wished for by housewives, also.

The technical term for organisms comprising material from two or more species is chimeras, a Greek term coined for the monsters of their imaginations: the mermaid, the centaur and so on. Within a few years we may actually see such chimeras. If the mind recoils a little at the prospect of an ape with human hands, it is because all departures from the natural order produce this effect at first. Europe was stunned when it first en/countered the rhinoceros, and stunned again by the kangaroo. Now we all take them for granted, and the objection to artificial chimerism will probably subside as soon as it has become familiar.

There is one further possibility, however, which may be much harder to accept, the formation of artificial symbiotes. It is already possible to join the circulatory systems of two mammals, including men. At present the only motives for doing so are medical and experimental. It seems just possible that, in the more distant future, there might be reasons which would make it useful to fuse several animals into a single system, like conjoined twins or multiplets. It is perhaps more probable, however, that the linking of brains together, to create a super/brain, will be more useful than linking bodies – a possibility discussed in Chapter 5.

What is abundantly clear, at least, is that transplantation surgery could become a vast industry, limited in scope only by the supply of available skills. The biomedical field is likely to be one of the great growth areas of the future, and will be supported by a biomedical industry, whose shares will be the growth stocks of the future, just as electronics and pharma-ceuticals have provided many of the growth stocks of today. And public demand for such facilities will throw an overwhelming load on the medical profession – and on state medical services in countries where they exist – which will necessitate drastic changes of structure and new training and recruitment. Failure to achieve such changes fast enough could make biomedicine a major political issue of the future.

The semi-artificial man

Parallel with these attempts to implant natural organs have gone experi-ments in the implanting of artificial ones, and although these are currently limited (as noted earlier) to bones, arteries, and teeth, with the heart as an experimental possibility, it does not take a great leap of the imagination to see that this is only the opening phase of a development which could lead eventually to the extensive implanting of artificial organs of every kind.

What has delayed such a development until now has been the fact that the body does not readily tolerate the presence of inorganic materials. Often local reactions occur and the body attempts to encase the im-planted material in a fibrous sheath. This is a useful defensive reaction when the foreign body is a fragment of shrapnel, say, but inconvenient when it is an implant. In some cases blood-clotting occurs: blood is a sensitive fluid and even contact with plain glass, one of the most inert of substances, will cause it to clot. (When blood is circulated through heart-lung machines clotting has to be prevented by the addition of anti-coagulants.)

The invention of the silicone materials, with their curious slippery surfaces, and of the tetrafluoroethylenes – they are known to most people under trade names such as Silastic and Teflon – marks a breakthrough, since the body tolerates them well, and no doubt even better variants will be produced in due course. It is this which has made artificial hearts and arteries practical, while stainless steel and even ceramics can be used where strength and rigidity are called for, as in joints or jaw-bones.

Whether the artificial organ will be competitive with the natural implanted organ – and if so, when – is difficult to foresee. The answer depends on whether the supply of natural organs is adequate, and this in
turn depends on the success with which storage methods are developed as
well as on the development of appropriate legislation for using cadaver
material. Public feeling about the use of animal organs may also be a
factor.

A good many years must pass, also, before it becomes clear which is
the more durable. The mechanical organ cannot be attacked by disease,
but it has its own problems and, like most machinery, will need servicing.

Eventually, nevertheless, it may be that some of these prostheses will
be developed to the point at which they represent an improvement on the
natural article, at least in some respects. A metal heart might have a
greater output than a human one, an advantage at high altitudes or for
prolonged exertions. One day an athlete with a metal heart, perhaps
supplementary to his own, may outstrip his undoctored opponents,
opening new vistas in sport. Such a heart might also aid men in extreme
situations, such as astronauts making a repair in space. Better lungs would
also be useful. A lung which will work under water is being developed at
General Electric's Schenectady research laboratories, and one can see that
it might be welcomed by nuclear submariners, for instance.

But it would be unimaginative to suppose that the artificial organ
makers will stop short at merely imitating existing organs. They will
certainly try to improve on them and may invent some absolutely new
ones. If one is going to have an artificial hand, one may as well have seven
fingers or two thumbs, if there turns out to be any advantage in it. Or
maybe you could have interchangeable hands on a plug-in basis, with
webbed ones for swimming and non-inflammable ones for heaping coals
of fire.

Work on a 'muscular system' which will outdo human muscles is
already in hand. Under development at Cornell Aeronautical Laboratory, Buffalo, for the U.S. Navy and Air Force is a 'man-amplifier'.
Like a lobster, which carries its skeleton outside its flesh, not inside as we
do, the amplified man wears a steel 'exoskeleton' powered by hydraulic
motors instead of muscles. Inside it he wears a light framework equipped
with sensors which sense his every movement and cause the exoskeleton
to repeat or follow it instantaneously. Preliminary designs called for the

man-amplifier to be able to support a load of 1000 lb. (half a ton) on either hand. Eventually, of course, such amplified men will be able to cope with much greater loads: to lift an automobile with one hand will be child's play.

Unfortunately, most of the power sources currently available (compressed gases, electric motors, etc.) rely on rapid rotatory movement and develop very little power at low speeds. Muscles, in contrast, exert a considerable effort relatively slowly and in a straight line. The hydraulic units employed for the prototype man-amplifier proved awkwardly bulky. But at the Weizmann Institute of Science in Israel, artificial muscles, which contract as real muscles do, are under development, and something on these lines will no doubt prove the answer for the powered exoskeleton, and also for the prosthetic arms now being designed for amputees.

This sort of development has led some prophets to foresee the emergence of a new relationship between man and machines, a relationship in which the two become so intermixed as to be virtually indistinguishable. The word 'cyborg' (an abbreviation of cybernetic organism) has been coined for such hybrids. The essential difference between tools and cyborgs is that the communication between them is two-way. The machine not only receives instructions from the man but also informs the man of the conditions it is encountering, just as his own hands or feet do.

Ralph S. Mosher, of General Electric, prefers to speak of the CAM concept, for Cybernetic Anthropomorphic Machines, and for this company he built 'Handyman': two arms and hands which repeat on a larger and more powerful scale anything that their master does with his arms and hands. Each hand has ten independent motions, but the key feature is that the mechanical muscles feed back to the operator the resistances they encounter. A robot without this 'force feedback' feature, trying to open a door, would probably tear the handle off. To open a door, one must let one's hand follow the arc of the door handle. One robot handler (made by another company), which lacked this device, attempted to punch a button on the wall and pushed the wall down. 'Handyman' can twirl a skipping rope; in doing this you have to sense from the varying pull on the rope the right instant to put more energy into it, so that a robot without feedback could not do this.

When I went to visit Dr Mosher, I saw 'Handyman' pick up a small child and put her down again. The non-feedback type of handler might have crushed her or sent her through the roof.

Inspired by the success of Handyman, General Electric are building for the U.S. Army a 'pedipulator' or walker, which will enable its wearer to take giant strides across country, as if on stilt-long legs. But unlike stilts, his metal legs will have knee and ankle joints, and will con-vey to him information about his balance. For the future, they see a combination of these devices, with which a man will be able not only to walk and grasp objects, but to swim rivers or swing from branch to branch. Clearly these are not machines – they only function when a man is functioning – they are man-amplifiers.

In the ordinary way it seems unlikely that men will want to maintain a relationship with these devices longer than is necessary. But in the alien conditions of another planet, they may need to live with them for weeks. To put a man in a clumsy and weighty space-suit and then ask him to climb into a vehicle may prove less sensible than to make his space-suit his vehicle also. (On the moon, with its weak gravitational force, the weight of space-suits and oxygen equipment is not so important, but on large planets they could become too heavy for a man to move in.) With his customary prescience, H. G. Wells foresaw this development; in *The War of the Worlds* the Martians are spider-like creatures which spend almost all their time in three-legged metal pedipulators.

The second of the developments which contribute to the cyborg con-cept is the growing use of mechanical prostheses. As long as artificial kidneys and heart-lung machines are so bulky they must remain external to the body; but they could be built into man-amplifiers, thus restoring to the wearer his lost mobility. The partially paralysed patient could also be given mobility and a wider range of activities by such a procedure.

At the same time, the past few years have seen the development of the first artificial arms controlled by currents from the wearer's muscles. The wearer simply thinks of raising his arm, and up the artificial arm goes. When the original limb is amputated high up, so that the operating muscles are removed as well, the signal can be taken from other muscles, so that the wearer may have to think of shrugging his shoulders in order to raise his arms, but this the brain is quite good at doing. As with the muscle-amplifier, the limiting factor on these 'myoelectric' prostheses, at present, is lack of a really satisfactory power source. Bottles of liquefied gas are chiefly used, which are on the heavy side, and last only a few hours. But the storage of power is being steadily improved, and it is unlikely this problem will remain unsolved for long.

Put these two concepts together – the CAM and myoelectric control – and we can picture a man embedded in a machine which does what he wants as soon as he thinks about it, without any muscular intervention on his part. The machine becomes, in a more literal sense than ever before, an extension of man. Here, still more, lies hope for the paralytic patient and it is reasonable to expect that one day paraplegics and others, if they can't be cured, will permanently inhabit a sort of metal body.

But this argument can be taken to a still more extraordinary stage. The brain itself (which, as we shall see in Chapter 6, can now be maintained outside the body) could be placed in such a metal body, which would be equipped with the necessary devices for perfusing it with blood, lymph and so on, and could then live indefinitely, until overtaken by its own senility. This we might christen 'total prosthesis'. While such a development may well be a century or more in the future, it is not to be dismissed as pure fantasy. It will certainly raise ethical, not to mention social, problems. Presumably it would be murder to refuse such a total prosthesis to anyone demanding it, and it would be suicide not to demand it. Society would therefore find itself faced, in a much more specific way than is now the case with dialysis machines, with an obligation which must certainly prove exceedingly costly.

A variant on this pattern can be foreseen in the current development, for space purposes, of 'slaves' or robot doubles. The idea, advanced by William E. Bradley of the Institute of Defense Analyses in Washington, is simply to take the robot handler just described and introduce a radio link between it and the operator. The radio link would carry sound and television signals, instructions from the operator to the slave and force feedback from the slave to the operator. In this way, an astronaut could sit within his spacecraft, while his slave went out into space to make a repair or to link up equipment – the advantage being that the slave requires no oxygen supply, heating or other maintenance while there, and is impervious to radiation, while danger to the astronaut is minimized. Equally, slaves could be sent out on the surface of the moon; if one dropped into a crevasse, it could be replaced by another. To make life more difficult, Bradley has named his proposed slave a 'telefactor'.

Owing to the time lag in signals, it would not be really practicable to send such slaves to the moon and control them from earth, but it would be possible to control aircraft or spacecraft in orbital flight in this way, or to control slaves on the moon from a spacecraft in moon orbit. Even on the earth, such slaves would be particularly useful in radiation fields which would be damaging or lethal to man, and some of the development work on them has been financed for this reason.

Applying this concept to the medical and civil situations we have been envisaging, we can see that, before it becomes possible to put a brain in a fully mobile body, it should be possible to provide it with a slave. The brain would then repose in sterilized surroundings, where it could be perfused by apparatus which might still be bulky, and could be watched over by medical attendants continuously, while its slave went to board meetings, played chess or dined with friends, continuously relaying the appropriate stimuli back to its owner, and responding to his commands. (It is to be hoped that interference-free radio channels will be available by this time!)

It seems unlikely that the tremendous technological effort involved in such a feat would be made available in the lifetime of anyone now living, except perhaps in one circumstance. It may not be quite out of the question that a paranoid dictator, finding himself afflicted by a slowly developing but mortal disease such as cancer, or simply by old age, should attempt to prolong his domination by such methods. I do not suggest that it would happen today: the time required to develop the equipment would be longer than a man in such a position could afford to wait. But in fifty years, when the technologies are fully developed, when slave-handlers have been perfected for space purposes and when ectopic brain maintenance is a commonplace, the final step of bringing them all together need not take very long.

At this point, the question, raised earlier, of the right to die, may raise its head. The ectopic brain (to coin a phrase, for we have no word at present for such a situation) of the paranoid dictator may find life in these conditions unbearable and regret his decision. But his aides may think his continued existence politically indispensable – as is often held to be the case in wartime – and decline to cut off the juices which maintain his existence, a situation of classic irony.

There is also a third development which has contributed to the cyborg concept – the development of the computer. Man and machine are here developing what must be called an intellectual relationship, at present best seen in the teaching-machine approach. Computers have been used to teach medical students diagnosis, putting to them the symptoms and commenting on their replies and further questions just as a human teacher would. At present such dialogues take place through a type-writer keyboard, the student's observations being typed in, and the machine printing out its answers.

Within a quarter of a century, however, we shall see the machine listen to spoken questions and enunciate its replies.

This aspect must also be placed in conjunction with those previously outlined. The computer, in principle, can also be given slave extensions, or placed in metal pedipulating bodies. When this occurs, we have the robot of Čapek's imagination. But the slave-equipped robot will come long before the fully mobile one, and computer-controlled manipulators already exist in the laboratory stage.

Finally, we can add to this series of extrapolations the converse of the notion of placing mechanical part in a living body, *viz.* the placing of living parts in a mechanical body. The suggestion that brains should be placed in CAMs is one instance; but it is not inconceivable that a human arm, or at any rate an ape's or a monkey's, could be coupled to a computer. (An ear or eye might be more difficult.) In short, a complex marriage seems to be taking place between man and machine. The science-fiction writer Isaac Asimov has foretold the establishment of a new race of man-machine hybrids; one day it may become impossible to tell whether one is talking to a mechanized human being or a human-ized machine. Or even which one is oneself.

Who am I?

This line of development fills many people with a deep sense of alarm, because it raises the question of personal identity. The question 'Who am I?' probably occurs to all of us at some point in life, and usually quite young. It may be said to mark a person's emergence as an individual. Philosophers of the personalist school, such as Martin Buber, or Husserl, not to mention existentialists such as Sartre, have devoted much attention to this basically unanswerable question. In so far as an answer can be given, today it generally takes the line: 'You are an unique individual, unlike any other in the universe, and your name, X, denotes that precise aggregation of qualities which you possess and no others.' Our sense of personal uniqueness would suffer a severe blow if we learned that, in some universe parallel to our own but inaccessible to us, every individual on earth had his precise counterpart or twin. Even though the inhabitants of this other world could not communicate with us, so that their existence could never affect us directly, we should find it hard not to think from time to time: how would my double behave in this situation? Or perhaps: I am determined to differentiate myself from him by doing something different from what he would do in this situation.

Consequently, if we acquire prosthetic organs which are identical with those carried by other people, we may feel the less unique, the less ourselves. It has been claimed that we shall also feel some dilution of ourselves when we carry a kidney or other organ donated by another. Probably, as the situation becomes commoner, this response will become weaker or fade away. Man seems to have a considerable power of assimilating machinery to himself: it has often been observed that people come to regard their cars as extensions of themselves, and even modify their kinaesthetic responses to include it. A man who has driven a car for some time 'feels' where the limits of his car lie and can steer it through a narrow gap almost as well as he could steer his body: when he takes over a new car, for some days, it 'feels strange' and his awareness of its limits and capabilities is lost.

Indeed, there is a sense in which even our bodies are only machines which we drive, and the limits of our identity are coterminous with the brain. An amputee, however much he regrets the handicap, does not feel that he is to any degree dehumanized as a person. But other people may. Many people feel a certain horror in meeting an amputee and an unjustifiable sense that he is somehow less than human. So cyborgs are likely to arouse these unconsciously motivated fears. And when Dr Comfort asks: 'Could even a disembodied brain be more "sinister" than a similar head attached to a paralysed patient in an iron lung?' the answer may well be 'yes'.

The question 'Who am I?' comes second only to the question 'Who are you?' As some psychologists have recently emphasized, we all feel deep anxieties when we encounter another human being in any kind of interpersonal relationship. Do they represent a threat to us, physically, emotionally, in terms of status, or in any other way? Shall I be able to meet their demands – for if not, I suffer in my own self-respect as well as in their eyes. If they represent a threat, or even a challenge, at any of these levels, shall I be able to cope with it?

It is because of this group of basic reactions, deeply built into all of us, that many people fear the robot, the zombie and the computer. They have no experience in dealing with their demands, which are by definition to some extent different from genuinely human demands; what is worse, they are uncertain even what these demands exactly are. Anyone who has had to deal with insane, or even highly neurotic, individuals will know the sense of fear and helplessness which assails one, as one realizes that all the normal human techniques for influencing others – persuasion, threat, reward, punishment, etc. – have no effect or even quite the wrong effect. The same kind of feeling in a much milder form is felt when we first try to control some unfamiliar machinery and it does something we don't expect.

But if we fear the intelligent machine, it is quite natural to fear even more the object which looks like a human being but turns out not to be one. This, I am sure, is the source of the revulsion many people feel at the prospect of man-machine hybrids. The idea of a computer which bursts into tears and demands affection is a little harassing, since we don't know how to comfort it, but we can relieve ourselves of the responsibility by remembering that it is 'only a machine'. Much harder to cope with, I suppose, is an android, which we treat with the circumspection due to a human being, expecting a similar degree of consideration in return, only to find that it is unaffected by human emotions, insensible to the pain or misery which it may cause, planning its actions in wholly logical terms of material advantage.

If the robot is equipped with a simulacrum of human emotions – and experiments to this end are already under way – the overt situation may be improved, since they are less likely to act 'inhumanly' and so to cause unintended suffering. But the psychological situation is worsened, for the fear remains that at some point the programming will prove inadequate; and the damage done, we anticipate, will be all the worse if we have been put off our guard and have lowered our defences.

The situation will be something like having a dog of uncertain temper, normally friendly but occasionally liable to snap even at its master. Only if years of experience prove that unpredictable reactions are rare in robots will they become fully acceptable. For a time, we must expect to see headlines in our newspapers which echo the personal disasters which we manage to tolerate today: ROBOT'S ERROR STARTS FIRE, or BERSERK ANDROID SLAYS FOUR, and even WEDDING STOPPED: BRIDE EXPOSED AS 'NOT FULLY HUMAN'.

But when the robot and the human being become indistinguishable, we are driven back to less logical fears, and the question 'Who are you?' may become unanswerable, just as it does should we encounter an alien intelligence or a being from another planet. And when that other proves to be stronger, more intelligent and equipped with a far wider range of sensory and effector organs, our fear is bound to be intensified.

In conclusion, I believe one should stress the real danger of the human race becoming divided into two classes: the haves (who have the advantages of modern prosthetics) and the have-nots (who struggle along with nothing but what nature provides). Frantic efforts will be made by the have-nots to cross the divide, but in the nature of things the effort will rarely be successful, and the gap will steadily widen and become harder to cross. Criminal methods will often be employed. Perhaps renegade surgeons, blackmailed or deprived of their will by drugs, will be used to rob privileged haves of their prosthetic devices and to implant them in the unprivileged have-nots. In some countries, no doubt, the state will decide who is to be promoted to the privileged class, and there may be degrees of privilege. Manual workers will have exo-skeletons, athletes will have spare hearts, and computer programmers spare heads. Only the head of state will have all the advantages. Outstanding workers may be rewarded by a licence to acquire an additional prosthesis, and laggards punished by removal and down-grading. In other countries, costly prosthetic devices may be leased, so that one can enjoy a wider range of experience for a time. The leasing of under-water swimming equipment today provides an exact analogy. These speculations should not be dismissed too quickly as merely fanciful.

4

Is Death Necessary?

In 1940, a British locomotive driver fell from his engine to the ground. The fall did not injure him in any obvious way but – as he put it – everything 'became hazy'. From being a man of powerful physique, aged 40, he rapidly became so weak that he could not even feed or dress himself. He lost both sexual desire and potency and felt himself to be 'an old man'. For a while after the accident he had fits of shivering and spells of weeping. His appetite faded and he slept badly. He became irritable and querulous. Then his hair began to fall out until, six months after the accident, he was completely bald. It was no exaggeration to say that he had aged almost overnight.

After rest and hospital treatment he recovered a little: his potency returned, though not his desire, and some hair grew upon his head. But he remained feeble, apprehensive and self-pitying. This once virile man had become a wreck.

This episode shows with unusual vividness that ageing, in the sense of loss of vigour and tone, both physical and psychological, is not simply a result of chronological age. You recognize this whenever you speak of a man being 'old before his time' or of a woman as 'young for her age'. On what, then, does ageing depend? If only we knew, we could probably bring some influence to bear on it. And if ageing can be accelerated, it is reasonable to suppose that it can also be retarded, if not actually stopped or reversed. This glowing prospect is attracting a growing volume of scientific research today. And there is no field of biological research, in my view, which could have more immediate and dramatic effects on human existence, both directly and indirectly.

The attitude of many gerontologists (as those who study ageing are called) is highly optimistic. According to Dr Alex Comfort, the director of Britain's Medical Research Council Gerontology Group, 'there is the real possibility of a breakthrough affecting either human vigour at high ages, or the human life span, or both. I think that even while it remains speculative, the public and administration should realize that that possibility exists, and that large numbers of scientists are engaged in trying to bring it about.' And he adds the warning: 'Like the Bomb in the past, and many other less dramatic but as fundamentally life-changing possibilities latent in the biology of the future, it now risks catching us unawares. . . .'

Professor A. L. D'Abreu, an expert in open-heart surgery, who is in charge of the Department of Surgery at Birmingham University, is another who takes an optimistic view. In a lecture in 1966 at the Royal College of Surgeons, he told his listeners that some of those present would probably live to be 180, as one result of the contemporary revolution in science and medicine.

It is true that the number of scientists working on the problem is large, and immensely larger than thirty years ago. It has been reckoned that more than a thousand teams clock in on such work in the U.S. alone. Nevertheless, I have the impression that Dr Comfort may be over-optimistic when he declares that we could 'within, say, twenty years at the outside, be in a position to know the nature of the predominant age-process in man.' As I see it, the research situation at the moment is that the decks have been cleared for action, so to speak; the nature of the problem has been redefined far more clearly than before, although virtually nothing has been done towards solving it. Optimism is common at such moments, but often physiological problems turn out to be more complex than one expects.

Comfort's prophecy cited above makes clear that the problem may be a double one. On the one hand we might hope to extend the whole span of life, so that, instead of dying, on the average, around three score years and ten, we might all hope to live hundreds of years, like Methuselah, provided we were spared by accident and disease. On the other hand – and this is perhaps the more immediately likely prospect – we might find out how to fight off the decline in vigour and resilience which starts in our twenties, and in some respects at birth, so as to remain 'young' until an advanced age, but without extending the average span of life. But

whether these are really two problems or merely two aspects of one problem is still uncertain. To gain some impression of what control of ageing
involves, let us look a little more closely at the ageing process.

Eternal youth

To live on as a greybeard, ever feebler, ever more arthritic, one's
senses fading, one's powers seeping away, like one of Shaw's ancients,
is an unattractive prospect, whatever the means used to realize it. For
most people, the maintenance of bodily vigour up to the limit of the
normal life span offers a far more attractive ambition.

To retain the energy and resilience of youth is something universally
desired. More than two centuries ago the great Dutch doctor van Boer-
haave, whose fame was so great that even Chinese emperors sent to
consult him, summed the matter up in these words: 'To hold to an un-
failing bodily health, a constant vigour and tranquillity of mind, and to
preserve these into a green and rugged old age until, without sickness or
struggle, body and soul part company!' This, he says, is more to be
desired than the Philosopher's Stone, which turned lead to gold.

But what happens in fact is very different. Between the ages of 30 and
90, the weight of our muscles falls by 30 per cent and the power we can
exert likewise. Even more significantly, the number of nerve fibres in a
nerve trunk falls by a quarter. The weight of our brains falls from an
average of 3·03 lb. to 2·27 lb., as cells die and are not replaced. The
nephrons in our kidneys, which eliminate waste substances from the
blood, fall in number to almost half. (We can observe the results of this in
the prolonged hangover caused by drinking amounts of alcohol which
would not have worried us in youth.) Even the taste-buds in the tongue,
which average 245 per papilla in youth, dwindle to 88 in the 90-
year-old. And as our capacity to taste declines so, as a rule, do our sight
and hearing.

At the same time, the functioning efficiency of the body falls. As
muscular power dwindles, our heart pumps less blood and takes longer
to recover from exertion. The fall is considerable: at 90 the amount of
blood pumped has fallen almost to half what it was at age 20. The lungs
pass less air, yet have to handle more to extract a given volume of oxygen.
Here the loss of efficiency is even greater: less than half that at 20 by age 75.

At the cellular level, too, this loss of efficiency is also seen. Nerve fibres conduct impulses up to 15 per cent more slowly: our reaction times lengthen. Even our nails grow more slowly. As has been said, the body dies a little every day.

Why is this? In the last few years it has become clear that, almost certainly, it is due to the random failure and eventual death of individual cells, one after another, throughout the tissues of the body. This failure particularly affects those tissues where the cells lose the power of replacing and renewing themselves by division: that is to say, nerve and muscle cells particularly. People die most often of heart failure, rather than liver failure, because the heart is made of muscle and when the cells in the heart-muscle die, they are not replaced. (Indeed, products of the dead cells may even poison the remaining healthy ones.) On the other hand, the liver does not lose the power of division; and if a piece is cut out it replaces it just as well in old age as in youth. It takes a severe stress on the liver (from a virus, for instance, or from alcohol) before a man dies of liver failure.

This 'cell death' theory of ageing has been given a solid foundation by Dr Nathan Shock, chief of the Gerontology Branch of the National Institutes of Health in Bethesda, Maryland, probably America's leading expert on ageing. In 1958 he launched a continuing study of 400 men at his laboratory in the Baltimore City Hospitals. The study is planned to continue for twenty years, but has already thrown new light on the problem.

Before they actually die, no doubt, cells function less and less well – as is suggested by the slower conduction of nerve fibres or by the longer time it takes the body to recover from stress at higher ages – which contributes to the loss of vigour with age.

Various reasons why cells should die have been suggested. The most likely theory is perhaps that suggested by John Bjorksten, a Finnish chemist now settled in the U.S.A., some twenty years ago: the long-chain molecules which, as we shall see, carry out the most important tasks in the cell become literally balled-up. Stray molecules or fragments of molecules become accidentally attached to the chain at various points, and the same molecules also attach at others, thus tying two points in the chain together. Sometimes – for instance, as a result of the impact of radiation – the chain may even stick to itself. Chemists have shown that insoluble products do appear in the cell and seem to be composed of protein-like material, and there is even direct microscopic evidence for these 'age pigments', as some workers call them. It is rather as if we should drip glue into a fine watch.

Earlier guesses, that the cell ran out of some essential ingredient (the 'out-of-gas' theory) or that it became clogged with its own waste products (the 'clinker' theory) do not fit the facts nearly so well. More plausible was the idea that radiation damaged the DNA, causing mutations which were likely to be lethal or which made nonsense of the hereditary message. But recent work tends to show that mutagens (i.e. chemicals which cause mutations) do not age mice, and extensive studies of the effect of radiation on mice and other small animals suggest that, unless the radiation dose exceeds a certain minimum considerably above that found in natural conditions, there is no general shortening of life or ageing effect.

If the Bjorksten 'cross-linking' theory is correct, are there any practical steps we could take to prevent ageing from cell death?

Bjorksten thinks there might be. He believes that there must be soil bacteria which can dissolve cross-linkages, arguing that we should find more fossilized proteins of this kind than we do if they were not being eroded. And, in this case, he concludes that we could not merely expect to delay ageing, we might actually be able to arrest cell death altogether and thus achieve immortality. Not all gerontologists would agree, and Dr Comfort declares roundly that there is 'no reasonable prospect of securing effective personal immortality for anybody in the foreseeable future. . . .'

This theory, be it noted, explains both the loss of vigour and the eventual death by the same mechanism. Death occurs when too many cells have died, and it makes sense that many people die of heart disease, when we remember that the heart is the most essential muscle and that muscle cells cannot be replaced. On the other hand if people subject some other vital organ to severe strain, or if it is weakened by infections, it may be the first to go. So, a remedy for cell death would preserve youthful vigour as well as prolonging the life span, if Bjorksten is right.

But, alas for certainty, there are some other facts which this theory does not explain – notably the kind of 'ageing overnight' described at the beginning of this chapter. We must therefore look at the question of life span a little more closely.

Allotted span

The facts which any theory of ageing has to explain are quite puzzling, when you stop to think about them. First there is the fact that every species has a distinctive life span and these cover a very wide range, from the single day of the mayfly to the 150 years of large tortoises and perhaps turtles. If the cells of mayflies run out of gas or clog up in a single day, how can those of tortoises continue to function for 150 years – nearly 50,000 times as long? Then again the life span, with one exception, seems to be roughly proportional to body weight; the bigger the body the longer the life. (The popular belief that carp live to great ages appears to be false.)

The exception is man, who lives about three times as long as he ought to on this basis – which has led to the suggestion that life span is also related to brain weight.

Despite the stories which circulate periodically of men who have lived to be 150 or more, there are no reliably documented cases of anyone living nearly so long. Britain introduced the compulsory registration of births as long ago as 1834 and no case of anyone living past 109 has been recorded since then. The oldest man for whom there is adequate documentary evidence is probably Pierre Joubert, a bootmaker of Quebec, who was born in 1701 and died in 1814, having lived 113 years and 120 days.

The age-mortality figures show a peaked curve: life span tends to be about 70 years; as you move to lower or higher ages, the number dying at each age falls off steadily, when the effects of disease and accident are allowed for. This is what would be expected on a cell-death theory, or on an out-of-gas or clinker theory for that matter. But there are other kinds of dying which follow a quite different pattern. For example, in many plants the leaves fall after the flowers have appeared and formed seed. But if the flowers are removed as they appear, the plant carries on for weeks or months, producing more flowers, and the leaves remain in their place. So it was nothing in the cells of the leaves which caused them to wither and die: some instruction to do so must have come from elsewhere, at a moment determined by a biochemical process in the flowers. Is there, then, a 'senescence factor' or 'death protein'?

And plants are not the only organisms which show this sort of be‑haviour. To take an instance from another sphere, there are certain water creatures of the kind known as rotifers, 90 per cent of which expire within a few hours of laying their eggs. What brings about their death? Again, when the tadpole becomes a frog, its tail is resorbed. The indi‑vidual cells in it die, destroyed by the little vesicles known as lysosomes, which have been called by their discoverer, Christian de Duve, 'suicide bags'. Similarly, when the embryo is developing – and this goes for human embryos too – certain structures play only a temporary role; when their usefulness is past, they 'necrose' or die. Moreover, certain moths seem to expire in a 'programmed' way, as do the red cells of the blood, which have a short life, measured in days.

The salmon dies after spawning, and in this case we know why it does so. It suddenly develops Cushing's disease, a disease caused by an in‑creased output of the hormone ACTH. Apparently the salmon contains some internal 'clockwork' which turns up its pituitary controls at the time of migration, and the over‑stimulated pituitary causes the excessive output of ACTH. We still know little about such biological clocks.

Finally, of course, in the case of our own species, there is the pheno‑menon known as 'premature ageing', already mentioned, which also suggests that ageing is not simply the result of wear and tear or the process of decay but that it reflects the existence of some definite sene‑scence‑control mechanism. But one can see how a defect in this mechanism might lead to the kind of ageing overnight which I have described. Con‑versely, it might even lead to a 'failure to die', until loss of vigour from other causes, or disease or accident, supervened.

Facts such as these suggest that cells contain some definite self‑destroy‑ing mechanism: it looks as if lysosomes are the intruments of destruction, but the nature of the clock which initiates destruction is unknown. As a matter of fact, the notion of a 'programmed death' has been reversed by some scientists who think that cells have a programme for living, and die when they have run out of programme, just as a computer stops when it has done all it was asked to do. If so, evolution could be expected to select the programme so as to produce the life span most advantageous to the species.

If this conception of an inbuilt control of life span is correct, it is reasonable to expect that some day men will discover how to tinker with the control or substitute a longer-running programme, but at the moment, it must be emphasized, no one has a clue to how this could be done: a lengthened life span remains a purely theoretical possibility.

Some years ago cosmetic manufacturers pricked up their ears at reports of a 'Peter Pan hormone' discovered by insect physiologists. Some insects – butterflies are a well-known example – go through a larval stage and finally metamorphose, or change, into the adult form. The British physiologist Sir Vincent Wigglesworth discovered that metamorphosis is regulated by a special hormone, which he named ecdysone, and located the glands which secrete it, using as his experimental animal the blood-sucking insect *Rhodnius*. When the glands from a young larva are implanted into one which is about to metamorphose, it keeps on growing and remains a larva. Hence, when it finally does metamorphose, it becomes a giant insect.

It is therefore conceivable that the cessation of growth and onset of sexual maturity in man are controlled by a specific hormone. (It is certainly the case that the onset of puberty is controlled by the brain – for instance tumours of certain areas of the brain cause sexual maturity to occur as early as two years of age.) But few young people, one imagines, would be willing to buy the possibility of a slightly longer life at the price of postponing maturity and remaining locked in the role of teenager for ten years or more, leave alone the prospect of becoming a giant.

Aside from this instance, there is only one known method by which scientists have actually been able to prolong life span.

In the 1930's, C. M. McCay of Cornell University performed an experiment over which gerontologists have puzzled ever since. He took some rats which were 300 days old, place them on the minimum diet short of actual deficiency and compared them with another group fed at a level which maximized their growth rate. At 1,150 days, he restored the first group to a normal diet. Then all he had to do was to wait patiently until they had all died. The group on the reduced diet lived twice as long as the well-fed ones. Close analysis then revealed that what had happened was that these rats had matured late. The length of time for which they survived after maturity was no longer than usual.

Varying this approach, Frederick Hoelzel and Professor A. J. Carlson of Chicago made rats fast one day in three, which had the effect of extending their lives by 20 per cent. (Hoelzel was so impressed by this he took to fasting too.)

But the conclusion, which was widely drawn at the time, that ageing results from cessation of growth, is not supported by other facts discovered since. For instance, fish, which never cease growing, can also be induced to live longer by dietary restriction. Moreover, McCay's rats suffered from osteoporosis (fragile bones, a common disease of old people) and other defects. Maybe it is just as well that lengthening life does not mean merely lengthening childhood!

Dr Bjorksten's theory, however, can account for these findings: he believes that McCay's rats lived longer because they were consuming fewer of the glue-like molecules which effect cross-linkages in the big protein molecules on which the cell depends.

There are also some other well-known features of ageing which call for explanation. The classic expression of ageing is the greying of hair, and 'greybeard' has been used as a synonym of 'old man'. The loss of teeth is also highly associated with age, as is loss of vision. The last is also due to a hardening process; the lens of the eye is focused by muscles which compress it to the appropriate curvature. As the lens grows stiffer and the muscles weaker, this becomes harder to do. But the greying of hair and loss of teeth have until very recently been unexplained. Dr Philip Burch of the Medical Research Council Environmental Radiation Research Unit at Leeds University declares that these may fall into the category known as auto-immune responses. As I mentioned earlier, the body possesses mechanisms for recognizing foreign tissues and destroying them, hence graft rejection. Sometimes it makes a mistake, and starts to reject some of its own tissue. This is known as auto-immunity, i.e. immunity to oneself. Dr Burch has shown, by a sophisticated mathematical technique, that auto-immune diseases have an age-distribution which can be explained by the combination of a hereditary predisposition and a small number of random events (here one might think of radiation damage). And he has also shown that the age distribution of hair greying and teeth loss fits the same pattern. This presents gerontologists with yet another line of attack, and strengthens my own impression that the subject is still in a pretty confused state.

Finally, there is the kind of age effect that we notice in increased stiffness, and especially in the common complaint known as slipped disk. This is due to a hardening of the gristly tissue known as collagen, which separates the spinal disks, underlies the skin, and constitutes forty per cent of all the protein in the body. This hardens with age like rubber, and for much the same reason. Cross-links tend to form between the long molecules of which collagen is composed, so that they no longer slide freely over one another, and the tissue loses its elasticity. (There is also evidence that the proportion between the several kinds of protein of which collagen consists changes in middle life.) This explains why 'slipped disk' episodes are so common around the age of 40–50 under strains which could easily have been tolerated at an earlier age.

In laboratory experiments, it has proved possible to restore denatured collagen to normal, using extracts of connective tissue. It is not yet known what it is in the extract which does the trick. Though this is a true rejuvenation – actually the only true rejuvenation ever achieved – it involves the complete dissolution of the collagen to begin with, so it is not obvious how, if at all, it could be applied to living tissue. Conceivably, a solvent may be found which would carry the agent concerned into the collagen tissue a little at a time and gradually reconstitute it without reducing the patient to a jelly during the process!

The fact is, in all probability ageing is not a 'clinical entity'. Like cancer or rheumatism, it is not just one disease but several which ordinarily get lumped together because the visible effects are much the same.

For example, there are almost certainly emotional factors in ageing, and even emotional reasons for death itself. Any doctor can tell you of patients who, learning they have an incurable disease, 'turn their faces to the wall' and give up hope. The British surgeon Sir Heneage Ogilvie once said that he could look around a table at a group of men in their 50's and tell from their faces which of them would die of cancer. Since we know that the secretion of hormones is under emotional control, there is nothing too surprising in this. Cases where one of a married couple dies and the other loses all zest for living and dies soon after are also not too uncommon.

If, then, there is an emotional factor in ageing, the prolongation of life may conceivably be effected by psychotherapy, euphoriant drugs or whatever new means of mental prophylaxis the future may develop. Conversely, if the general character of life in the society of the future becomes more stressful or less satisfying, the prolongation of life may be made more difficult.

Taking a broad view, scientists describe the diseases which manifest in later life as 'degenerative diseases'. As the infections which used to polish people off in infancy or early life are brought under control, these degenerative diseases, which represent the body's gradual wearing out and the breakdown of parts, become more and more prominent. Among them, of course, is cancer – an unrestrained division of cells which may be compared with the racing of a watch when the escapement mechanism goes wrong.

At present, the only significant steps which can be taken to minimize the effects of ageing are the replacement of the broken components – and probably the provision of artificial or grafted heart, lung and liver replacements will make the biggest contribution to life prolongation in the years immediately ahead. But there are subtler forms of degeneration than organ failure. Particularly important is exhaustion of the hormonal messengers which control so many of the body's activities. Gerontologists have had some solid successes with hormonal replacement therapies.

Take the question of muscular strength. A man of 70 normally has only the strength he had when he was 12 or 13 – about half what he had in his late teens. Muscular strength depends upon the amount of muscle protein, and the body's ability to make protein depends closely on the body's supply of the male hormone, testosterone. By injecting old people with a combination of cortisone and testosterone, one can bring about an increase in strength of grip of as much as 47 per cent. Testosterone has the disadvantage, as far as women are concerned, that it produces a virilizing effect (and in men, prostate trouble), but there are now new synthetic hormones which have the proteinforming effect without the virilizing one. These socalled 'anabolics' also have useful sideeffects. They improve weight and arrest loss of bone substance, which may manifest as the disease known as osteoporosis. Some of the anabolics improve the elasticity of the skin, and no doubt have a future in cosmetics, if nowhere else. And in a few people an increase in alertness has also been reported. However, they must be used under close medical supervision, since they can activate latent disease of the prostate, cause water retention and have other undesirable effects.

Among the steroid hormones there is only one group the output of which falls off with advancing age. (They are known to chemists as the 11deoxy17ketosteroids.) All the members of this group, it has recently been found, are manufactured in the body from a single sub-stance, and it i. this process of conversion which begins to fail. Gerontolo-gists are therefore deeply interested to see what happens if you supply all the missing substances.

Before long, no doubt, it will be possible to implant the glandular structures which secrete such hormones and thus avoid the need for repeated injections.

But how far, and for how long, purely hormonal treatments will keep cells up to scratch in the face of continued cell death remains open to doubt. Despite the optimism of many gerontologists, it may prove that they merely fan the dying embers, bringing about a short-lived improve-ment in performance and well-being at the cost of bringing the final collapse even nearer.

However, there are two possible methods of prolonging the life span: one is hibernation. This might enable one to live to a greater chronological age, though without giving one any additional waking hours; indeed, it might conceivably reduce them. Another proposal which has been talked about a good deal recently is that human beings could be put in something resembling a deep-freeze and preserved for a while. Let us take a look at both these ideas, before turning to some other aspects of the battle against death.

Deep freeze

The proposal that human beings could be preserved alive by freezing would, it is pointed out, offer the possibility to people suffering from an incurable disease of waiting around until a cure was discovered. And it is true that if a person who died of pneumonia in 1920, say, had been pre-served until today, he could almost certainly have been saved.

If the process proved free from risk, others might wish to store them-selves for a while, simply in order to see the world of the future, or to see how their own children turned out (though the latter might disappoint them by being frozen themselves!) or even because they were passionately interested to know the solution of some scientific problem. And if they did not like the world they found, they could presumably return to the freezer for a second period. The social consequences of any such proposi-tion are obviously so fantastic and far-reaching that it is worth evaluating its practicability very carefully. Among the problems one can see arising are those of inheritance of property. Children expecting to inherit would be irked at being balked of their inheritance, and if they managed the property during its owner's glacial period would not like turning out on the specified date of his return to normal life. The incentive to postpone reviving him, on some excuse or other, would be, in many cases, over-whelming. A son who had taken over the management of a business owned by his frozen father and had expanded it, would not want to be ousted by the old man, and would have become dependent on the in-come it brought him, to say nothing of the prestige or social status.

Again, the Inland Revenue might suffer a considerable loss of revenue from a decline in death duties, and would perhaps attempt to discourage such ventures by a tax on absentee owners or their properties. One might ask too whether the law could insist on reviving a frozen individual required to give evidence in court, or one against whom a charge was to be preferred. And what damages might be brought against someone who revived a freezee against his will, if he died or was injured during his unwished-for visit to the land of the unfrozen?

The political situation remains somewhat obscure: would a freezee (someone is going to have to invent a name for them) have a vote? If so, could he leave it to a particular political party indefinitely?

Apart from these individual problems, there would certainly be a fantastic economic problem, or set of problems, if ever the practice became popular. The maintenance of the hibernacula, freezatoria, or whatever they may be called, with all precautions against infection, periodic inspection by medical staff of the freezees, and so forth, cannot be cheap. A decreasing number of active people might find themselves saddled with the task of maintaining an ever-growing accumulation of hibernating ones. Though some financial provision may have to be made by the candidate for glaciation, somebody has to do the work, and money in the bank is not the same thing. Inflation could reduce or wipe out the sums set aside by a freezee for his maintenance, and presumably he would then have to be awakened whether he wished it or not. However, the return to life of large numbers of people, unadapted to the society in which they find themselves, also presents problems. At the least, they will need re-training in the use of mechanical devices, which will have changed com-pletely, and will also need bringing up to date on the legal position.

(They may also be greeted by a considerable pile of unopened letters, bills, writs and other surprises.) At most they might completely unbalance the market, changing the pattern of demand and the supply of labour in a manner hard to predict. They will, of course, require outfitting with new clothes, and countless gadgets equivalent to the fountain pens, electric razors and wrist-watches of our own day, but more numerous, more intricate and more costly.

This prospect is being taken so seriously by some people that, in the United States, a number of societies have been formed to accelerate progress, notably the Life Extension Society of Washington, the Immortality Research and Compilation Association of California, and the Anabiosis and Prolongevity Institute of New York. Furthermore, a number of people have paid sums to ensure that, at death, their bodies will be preserved by freezing, in the belief that techniques whereby they can be revived will be shortly discovered.

Dr James H. Bedford, a retired professor of psychology, set aside $4,200 for this purpose before his death of cancer, at the age of 73, in California last year. The Cryonics Society of California advised, and Dr B. Renault Able performed the cryo-burial, if that is the word. The first step was the injection of an anti-clotting agent, heparin, after which the chest was opened and heart massage applied, so that the brain should be kept supplied with blood. As soon as possible Dr Bedford was transferred to a heart-lung machine and the body temperature lowered by packing with ice to 8° C. At this point most of the blood was withdrawn and replaced with a solution of salts plus the 'wonder solvent' DMSO, which I mentioned earlier in connection with skin storage. The temperature of the body was then lowered to $-79°$ C. and it was flown to Phoenix, Arizona, for storage at $-190°$ C. in liquid nitrogen. It will cost about £100 a year to maintain it at this temperature.

Dr Bedford did not imagine that no freezing damage would be caused, but believed that before too long scientists would find a way of repairing such damage, and reviving stored bodies. To aid in this, he left $200,000 to found the Bedford Foundation for Cryobiological Research. However, since DMSO has many adverse effects, not yet fully understood, his chances are slim, even apart from the problem of damage from the concentration of electrically charged fluids within his body cells. As Dr Stanley W. Jacob, the Associate Professor of Surgery at Oregon University, commented at the time: 'The poor man's funds have been wasted as far as his own chances are concerned.'

However, experts in the freezing of tissues are divided about the technical possibility of any such process. Possibly the world's leading expert is Dr Audrey Smith, of Britain's National Institute of Medical Research at Mill Hill, near London, known for her work on freezing the cornea of the eye for storage. She sees some hope of storing organs – and has done work on the lung. Professor A. S. Parkes, with whom she formerly worked, has predicted that organ storage may be achieved by 1971. But there is a world of difference between storing inert tissues like the cornea, or skin, and storing actively metabolizing cells, especially for long periods of time. There is evidence that certain membranes in the cell are only maintained by a process of continual reconstruction, and may disintegrate when the cell is brought to a standstill.

Early attempts to freeze organs and, still more, entire animals, were defeated by the formation of ice-crystals within the cells, which punctured the walls. The discovery that immersing the cell in a solvent such as glycerine and controlling the freezing rate very carefully could overcome this hazard led to the successful freezing of certain organs, as already described.

Certain cases where human beings have been frozen in natural circumstances give the impression that freezing of human beings is possible. Thus in 1960, a Russian tractor driver, Vladimir Kharin, who had become lost in a snowstorm, was found unconscious, stiff and blue, but without frostbite or putrefaction. It appeared that he had lain under the snow three hours, and it is thought he had been narcotized by the carbon dioxide in his own breath. Taken to hospital, he recovered and eventually returned to work. In Tulsa, Oklahoma, a similar incident was reported: a negro woman, found frozen stiff on a cold winter's night, was revived, despite some frostbite of her extremities. It is certain that the body temperature of these people did not fall to zero. The lowest level to which human body temperature has ever been depressed, with subsequent survival, is 9° C. This was during surgery with hypothermia. Normally such surgery takes place at about 25° C, against the body's normal 37° C.

Currently, the situation is that a mammal can be revived without ill effect after up to an hour's cold storage, by which time 50 per cent of the water in the body has turned to ice. As the water freezes, the concentration of the salts in what remains increases, with destructive effects, particularly on the cell membranes; moreover, the various cellular processes are slowed by different amounts, so that biochemical anarchy ensues. Not only rats and mice but dogs and monkeys have been revived after an hour of sub-zero body temperature, but rarely longer. Insects and bacteria are a different matter. Professor H. E. Hinton, of Bristol University, has frozen the larvae of midges for ten years and thawed them out, while bacteria can survive indefinitely under such conditions. Some bats can withstand sub-zero temperatures – they are, of course, hibernators – for reasons which are not clear. Even cold-blooded animals do not tolerate extensive freezing.

Desaturation of body fats seems to help hibernators, and may therefore help other mammals, if a means of bringing it about can be devised.* Probably the candidate for freezing will have to undergo elaborate preliminary rejigging of his body chemistry.

It is worth pointing out that the animal whose heart-beat and breathing have stopped is clinically dead, and hence that these experiments are experiments in the revival of the dead, medically speaking. The biologist escapes this paradox by jesuitically defining death as 'the state from which resuscitation of the body as a whole is impossible by any currently known means'. If it revives, it wasn't really dead. But since human beings thus long frozen may have suffered irreversible brain damage, the question of whether people frozen to death should necessarily be revived arises.

Russian workers claim to have pushed the process a little further, though not without the anticipated adverse effects on brain function.

The Russians started experimental work on this subject some twelve years ago, at the Laboratory of Experimental Physiology for Resuscitation, maintained by the Russian Academy of Medical Sciences, starting with dogs. They drained the animal's blood completely, and reanimated it after 5–6 minutes initially; subsequently the period was extended by stages to an hour.

More illuminating, I think, are the experiments performed on baboons at the Institute of Experimental Pathology and Therapy at Sukhumi in

* Many oils can take up hydrogen, whereupon they become solid, as when margarine is made from vegetable oils: this process is known as saturation. Conversely, butter left to go rancid desaturates and becomes oily. In general, animal fats are normally saturated, vegetable fats are not.

the Caucasus. The animals' temperatures were first reduced to about 24° C, and their blood drained. Kefa was the name of one of these baboons. Four hours after resuscitation she opened her eyes. After six hours she was playful enough to seize a syringe and run round the oper-ating theatre with it. Kefa retained her former food preferences, which argues that abstract memories were retained as well as skills. But not all the animals survived, and in some cases it took three months before the higher nervous activity was restored to normal after 30 minutes of 'death'. This is progress of a sort, since animals which had been dead only 2-4 minutes, without cooling, took 7 to 9 months to return to normal. In later experiments, the temperature was lowered further to 10° C, and the period of 'death' extended to two hours. But after this experience, it took twenty hours to restore hearing, three days to restore sight and seven days for total recovery. There was also some heart fibrillation (an irregular fluttering due to disturbance of the electrical impulses which control the heart-beat), a sign of imminent heart failure.

While it is rather remarkable that the body can rebuild the connections which have broken down at all, considering the limited adaptability of neurones, the prospects of surviving a prolonged 'death' without major damage and impairment, by the techniques available at present, seem remote, and it will be a brave man who first risks the experience. Since the brain seems to be the vulnerable spot, it may be that we shall have to think in terms of removing the brain and storing it separately from the body in different conditions. At Kobe Medical College, Japanese workers led by Professor I. Suda have recently reported some success with this. After removing the brain – that of a cat – it was cooled in a bath of glycerol and stored for no less than seven months at −20° C. Prior to this, the blood had been replaced with a glycerol solution, while the animal was anaesthetized. After restoring to normal conditions, 'approximately normal' electrical activity restarted, and the brain cells looked 'almost normal' under the microscope.

So we need not lose hope.

Professor A. S. Parkes declares: 'Science fiction notwithstanding, the prospect of suspending animation for indefinite periods in man by freezing him is remote.' But elsewhere he has given himself a saving clause: 'All this of course sounds fantastic, but we have learned to use the word "impossible" with caution. Ten years ago no normal mammalian cell had been frozen to temperatures compatible with long storage. Today this procedure is commonplace.'

If anything in this line is achieved, I conclude, it seems more likely that it will be by means of induced hibernation: a slowing of the bodily processes rather than a complete cessation. After all, we *know* this to be possible: nature does it regularly. Oddly enough, though, the mechanism of hibernation is still not understood and in fact very little work has been done on it until recently. Some species hibernate when closely related species do not. Among hamsters, there are both hibernating and non-hibernating varieties.

Dr R. R. J. Chaffee of the Department of Zoology at Missouri University has recently conducted some breeding experiments, breeding the hibernating and non-hibernating varieties of hamster for several generations. Before long, he had two populations of hamsters, one in which only 22 per cent of the animals hibernated and one in which 74 per cent did so. Before he separated the two strains, 57 per cent of his hamsters had hibernated. Thus he showed the habit to be under genetic control. Consequently, if we can learn how to alter the genetic message, on the lines discussed in Chapter 6, we can expect to be able to insert hibernation into the human repertoire. But we may not need to wait upon so radical a manoeuvre. For genes make enzymes and enzymes control the synthesis of proteins. So, somewhere along the line, if we can identify the enzymes and proteins involved in hibernation, we may find ourselves able to induce hibernation by injecting the appropriate substance.

Hibernation is distinct from sleep: the body temperature falls, in some cases to a couple of degrees above the freezing point of water. The heartbeat slows down to as little as three beats a minute and breathing may be reduced to one breath every three minutes. It is easy to see the appeal of this to the Space Agency. On a year-long journey to Mars, or an even longer trip to Jupiter, astronauts will have little to do, and will be very bored and lonely. If they could be induced to hibernate, this would eliminate the boredom, while greatly reduced supplies of food, water and oxygen would be required. Even at a body temperature as high as 68° F (against the normal 98·4° F) the human metabolic rate declines to 25 per cent of normal.

But there are more interesting possibilities than assisting astronauts to reach the planets. It has been suggested that overnight hibernation might be substituted for sleep. The human heart moves ten tons of blood a day against a resistance equivalent to a five-foot column of water. If the heart rate could be cut to, say, ten per cent of the normal level of 70 beats a minute every night, it might wear out far more slowly. So overnight hibernation (could we call it nighbernation?) might conceivably prolong life and by a very considerable extent. On the other hand, since many eliminatory and adaptive processes within the body would be slowed, one might not feel fully restored to vigour upon waking.

It may be significant that humming birds, whose temperature drops at night, greatly outlive shrews, which also have a high metabolic rate, but which have not acquired this trick. The humming bird's consumption of oxygen falls from 24 cubic centimetres per gram of body weight to 1 c.c./gm. It normally lives for about eight years – cases of 12 years are known. The shrew, in contrast, normally lives only six months, and rarely longer than three years. Some small hibernating bats live as long as twenty years, a remarkable figure, bearing in mind that life span is related to body size. Is hibernation, perhaps, the answer?

In his lively *Profiles of the Future*, Arthur Clarke picks A.D. 2050 as the date when suspended animation may come in. He may have been unduly pessimistic.

There are also broader social possibilities. Since the food requirement of the hibernating animal is so low, it has been proposed that, in times of famine, whole populations might be put into hibernacula and aroused when food supplies were normal again. But the costs of building and maintaining the hibernacula would be high, if not prohibitive, and in a famine-ridden country like India, one could hardly hope to store fifty or a hundred million people even for one year.

Moreover, when the question of terminating such mass hibernations became active, many of the non-hibernators might prefer to keep still limited supplies of food for themselves, rather than revive a myriad mouths and spread the ration thinner. 'Revivalists *v.* Survivalists' could one day be a bitter political issue.

Again, hibernation might prove attractive in the event of a serious release of radiation, due most probably to the explosion of nuclear weapons. Such a war might only be local, as smaller powers acquire the skills required to make such weapons, but the fall-out could nevertheless affect foodstuffs all over the world. In these circumstances, there would be a strong incentive to retire into a hibernaculum and so avoid the need to consume contaminated foodstuffs. (What more ironic situation can one conceive than that of a man obliged to eat food, or else die of starvation, knowing that the food he eats is contaminated and will eventually kill him?) If the number of hibernacula – or the supply of the hibernationinducing drug – is limited, there might be fierce competition for the facilities.

Leadshielded hibernacula might likewise provide a means of escape from the shortterm environmental radiation produced by nuclear war on one's own territory. In fact, what with one thing and another, hibernation may be a good word not to skip over when scanning the newspapers.

Social consequences

The social effects of these studies will depend on which matures first. If life can be lengthened, the most likely pattern is that which we should expect if the clock ran slower: a longer infancy followed by an extended youth, leading to a prolonged maturity and a prolonged old age. What we should like, no doubt, would be a prolonged maturity, a normal youth, and a shortened infancy and old age. But to mark time for a bit at maturity may be much harder to arrange.

The next most probable pattern is that of a prolonged prematurity – like McCay's rats. By giving longer to the schooling period, without cutting into the 20–30 period of maximum physical capacity, some benefit might be obtained. A prolonged immaturity would at least enable us to give more time to training, though in practice it might lead to a tendency to put people to work when less mature, since they would tend to continue starting work at the customary chronological age. Socially, it would be more valuable if we could 'mark time' during our maturity. Even a tenyear extension would greatly improve the ratio between the time required to train a man and the time during which he can make use of his training. As training gets longer and more costly, this becomes increasingly important. Already doctors spend some thirty years of their life attaining the required standard of skill and experience, and may have only another thirty or so to employ it.

A more discouraging aspect of the question is the likelihood that mental ageing may continue even if physical ageing is arrested.

Even if we can preserve the many kinds of cell which go to make up the body from the effects of age, there is no promise that we can preserve the neurones or brain cells in like manner. For brain cells do not divide (and a hundred thousand of them perish every day). Despite the brain's great margin of surplus capacity, this must eventually be exhausted, so that prolongation of life could mean a population of physically fit people with senile minds. So at least some scientists have argued, though if it is the brain which determines death, then this situation could, presumably, not arise.

Professor Donald McKay has suggested, furthermore, that our nervous system may have committed itself to principles matched to the life span of the body; thus, memory molecules may only have a limited life span, similar to the body's. We might therefore find ourselves populating the world with people who look young but are in fact increasingly senile. And Professor Koprowski, the Director of Philadelphia's Wistar Institute, has suggested that they may also be increasingly liable to infections.

Sir George Pickering, the Regius Professor of Medicine at Oxford, is one who takes this view. 'The goal of medicine', he said recently at a symposium on the future of medicine, '. . . is that of indefinite life, perhaps in the end with someone else's heart or liver, someone else's arteries, but not with someone else's brain. Should it succeed, those with senile brains and senile behaviour will form an ever-increasing fraction of the earth's population. I find this a terrifying prospect.' And he added: 'We may well ask ourselves whether it is not time to halt the programme of research and development which will make such a thing possible. . . . We must face up to the probable consequences of our ideas and ideals and be prepared to revise them.'

Even if senility can be averted, it is still the case that the thinking of the old becomes increasingly rigid; their decisions tend to be based on experience, yet their experience becomes progressively more out of date. It is said, for instance, that generals, in peacetime, spend their time preparing to meet the conditions of the last war. And, as the proverb has it, you cannot teach an old dog new tricks. Indeed, learning in general becomes more difficult with age, as those who have studied the problem of retraining older workers have discovered. The country which prolongs the average span of life of its population may have to take measures to press retirement in the industrial, administrative, scientific and other intellectual groups. Today, it is precisely in these groups that men often hold on longest.

Another probable consequence of the prolongation of life would be a further increase in the excess of women over men in the higher age groups of the population. Already between 65 and 69, there are 119 women for every 100 men (according to the U.S. Department of Health), although the margin becomes smaller at still higher ages. The trend to a kind of matriarchy which we can see already would be enhanced.

The old tend to be not only rigid but querulous and demanding, and the aged parent – often a grandmother – who dominates her children, using their expectations of inheritance as well as their natural affection as levers, already constitutes something of a problem. A society containing a large percentage of such 'dragons' would be quite intolerable.

While western society today is 'youth-centred' and the old are neglected, such developments might bring about a gerontocracy and an 'age-centred' society; it is difficult to see how the latter kind could be as vigorous as the former.

And as Dr Irving Wright of New York pointed out to the American Medical Association towards the end of 1967, if medical science were to find a cure for atherosclerosis, or hardening of the arteries, the prime cause of strokes and heart attacks, it would become difficult to predict how long people would live. Even today, there are more than 20 million Americans over the age of 65 and even some 12,000 over 100. As he stressed, we are moving towards a position where a progressively smaller proportion of the population is shouldering the burdens of all 'to an intolerable degree'. In Dr Wright's view, the age of retirement should be made ever later, not ever earlier. Very soon, 65 will be merely middle age.

But scientists are not only tackling the problems of ageing; they are even challenging death itself.

Arrested death

In 1966 a small girl, aged 11, died in a hospital in Liverpool. Six years earlier, when she was only five years old, she had been run over by a car.

Throughout these years a team of skilled people had, at enormous cost, maintained her vital functions, except for that of consciousness. In the end these efforts failed to keep at bay the consequences of inanition, and she 'died'.

A year previously, the Algerian Foreign Minister, Mr Khemisti, was shot through the head by assassins. His breathing stopped and his brain suffered irreversible damage from lack of oxygen. Taken to hospital, he was pronounced clinically dead. But he was connected to a heart-lung machine, and his body continued to function, after a fashion – at least it did not decay – and he 'lived' for a further three weeks, defying the summons of death.

The Russian Nobel prizewinner, Lev Landau, 'died' no fewer than four times under such extracorporeal circulation, after being severely injured in a motor accident. After nearly four months of unconsciousness, he was finally restored to something resembling health, though his mental faculties are reported to be much impaired.

Such incidents will become steadily commoner, and the length of time for which the reprieve is won will be steadily extended. What we are seeing here is the early stages of a development which will lead to the power to maintain alive indefinitely people who would formerly have died from wounds or other lesions. The heart-lung machine is only one weapon in the armoury. Massive blood transfusions save those who would have died of loss of blood. Intravenous feeding often maintains comatose patients who would otherwise starve to death. In some motor accidents, and rather commonly in motor-cycle accidents, the nerves running to the brain are sheared by the sudden deceleration on impact. The victim has in effect broken his neck, except that the bone, gristle and muscle are still in good order. Such people have been maintained alive for as long as three years. Since the nerves to the eyes and face muscles do not shear, they can often blink, focus their eyes and show other signs of life. When they die, it may be from inanition – it is difficult to maintain bowel action in the motionless patient and muscles in general lose tone. Electric stimulators will probably overcome this, and soon it will be possible to maintain such people in their living prison for indefinite periods, perhaps for ever.

At best they must be desperately bored, and they are certainly useless; at worst they may be going through some kind of hell. Their incompletely purified blood may – though no one really knows – inflict intense headaches or deep depression. They may feel pain, which will seem to come from various parts of the body, but which originates in the severed nerve endings. As they sink into coma, they may, who knows, be plagued by a frightening dream or delusion. Yet to terminate their lives would be a crime, technically murder.

Some years ago a British doctor wrote to a medical journal, saying that he had just performed an operation on an elderly lady. Had she survived, she might have lived another ten years, hopelessly paralysed, a burden to herself, and to others – for to maintain a comatose patient requires the full time of two or three nurses. In this case, fortunately as the writer felt, the patient did not survive the operation. The question he put to his fellow doctors, however, was: is it really my duty to preserve 'life' in such circumstances?

This kind of situation may become more and more common: society may find itself maintaining more and more people for longer and longer periods in such states, for which the term 'arrested death' seems more appropriate than the term 'life'.

The fact is, the age-old distinction between 'dead' and 'alive' has broken down. And while we have people who are technically alive – if 'alive' is defined in terms of the heart beating – we also have people who are technically dead, since their heart has stopped, but who are not lost to life since they can be revived. Surgeons now draw a distinction between 'clinical death' and 'biological death'. Not very well-chosen terms: reversible death and irreversible death would express the distinction more clearly and precisely.

Many doctors think that brain function is a better criterion of death than heart function, and that death should be diagnosed on the basis of EEG (electroencephalograph) tracings of the brain's electrical activity. As the Boston neurosurgeon, Dr Hannibal Hamlin, puts it: 'Although the heart has been enthroned through the ages as the sacred chalice of life's blood, the human spirit is the product of man's brain, not his heart.' But in legal practice generally, as also by custom, the stopping of the heart is taken to be the sign of death.

The French, renowned for their icy logic, have already tackled this issue. In May 1966, by a unanimous decision, the French National Academy of Medicine decided that a man whose heart is still beating may be ruled dead. The Academy's decision, which was based on the report of a special commission set up four months previously, has the effect of permitting doctors to remove living organs for transplantation purposes from people who have no hope of survival. And it recommended that the demise should be confirmed by the electroencephalograph: if the brain shows no activity for 48 hours, the brain, and the patient, are to be assumed to be dead.

These attempts at a redefinition of death, however useful in the case of mortally injured persons, give the doctor no help in the case of the 'vegetable' type of patient, part of whose brain, at least, is still functioning. Neither do they help the doctor in the case of the slowly dying patient, whose end can be protracted unmercifully with modern techniques. Such a patient can be forcibly brought back from the brink of the grave a number of times before death claims him.

We must face the unpleasant fact that death protracted by such methods is usually visibly more painful than if the patient had been denied the treatment. Charles F. Zukosi III, surgeon at the Veterans' Administration Hospital in Nashville, Tennessee, observes: 'This is an agonal type of death. We can carry the prolongation of so-called life too far.' And as another doctor has urged, 'Let them die with dignity.'

Apart from the situation of the patient, the prolongation of death puts a massive strain on relatives. The patient's family not only suffer cruelly, but may have to pay as much as $250 a day for the use of the equipment, in the absence of a national health service. There is also, in the present conditions of equipment shortage, a dilemma for the surgeon. 'When do you pull the plug out and make this expensive equipment available to someone else who might live?' asks Dr Robert S. Schwab of Harvard.

Of course the problem is not an entirely new one: few doctors with terminal cancer patients who may be in great pain and whose death is a matter of days feel themselves obliged to throw in major medical resources to prolong their suffering. Many doctors solve this ethical problem by permitting themselves inaction while forbidding themselves any positive action. Thus they would not give a patient a drug in order to hasten his death but would feel free to withhold medication, should the patient develop a respiratory infection (as often happens) on top of his mortal illness. To many this will seem ethically unconvincing, even if it provides a useful rule of thumb in practice. And it makes little sense in terms of the new mechanical devices: once it has been decided to apply the respirator, one can never 'pull the plug out' since that is a positive action.

The ethical problem here is perhaps the most pregnant so far raised by the new biology, and has given rise to a Papal pronouncement, which was given before an audience of clinicians, surgeons and scientists on 24 November 1957. The main point was summarized by the Most Rev. Fulton J. Sheen, the Roman Catholic Auxiliary Bishop of New York, in 1964 in these terms: 'Life may be prolonged by either ordinary or extraordinary means, such as a battery of tubes and devices in a terminal cancer patient. No one is obliged to use such extraordinary means, and there would be no moral difficulty in asking that they be removed.' Though helpful, such a definition leaves a doubt as to what qualifies as 'extraordinary'. The extraordinary means of today become the ordinary means of tomorrow.

On the other hand, Dr Immanuel Jacobovits, Chief Rabbi of the British Commonwealth, says that Judaism 'emphatically denies' the right of the doctor to let his patient die in peace, since it derives its sanction from the Biblical 'thou shalt surely cause him to be healed'. But he qualifies this admirably clear statement by adding that Jewish law does not require the physician to prolong the patient's misery by *artificial* means. 'Artificial' remains undefined.

Apart from the religious aspect, even those who take a wholly prag-matic view will want to be sure that the doctor's new power of life and death is not abused, and that every case is considered on its merits. In Britain in 1967 a television producer, attending a hospital for a check-up, found an instruction had been issued to the hospital staff concerning the use of resuscitation equipment. Whole categories of people, notably those over a certain age, were automatically excluded from resuscitation treat-ment. He subsequently made a television programme which became front-page news. This kind of publicity, which activates fears and prejudices, is liable to make the introduction of a 'die-with-dignity' policy even harder than it is at present, but it gives us a foretaste of the kind of controversy which will become more and more common in future and demonstrates the importance of establishing acceptable ground rules.

Even the rather straightforward-seeming decision to disconnect the machine when the brain's electrical signals have ceased can lead to mis-understanding and alarm. At Massachusetts General Hospital, for instance, it is a rule of thumb that if the brain trace has been flat for 24 hours and does not respond to stimuli, such as loud noises, and if the patient has no heart-beat and respiration of his own, he can be pronounced dead and the equipment disconnected.

But when one of the world's leading heart-lung surgeons, Dr Clarence Crafoord of Sweden, made a similar suggestion in May 1966, there was a public outcry: people seem to have thought he meant that the machines maintaining patients should be switched off so that their organs could be used for transplantation purposes. He was, of course, referring only to the hopeless cases, but the incident suggests that some measure of public education may be necessary.

More than a century ago, Arthur Hugh Clough wrote, with bitter irony:

> Thou shalt not kill; but needst not strive
> Officiously to keep alive.

He intended to satirize the way men were left to die of malnutrition and lack of medical care. Today, his words have taken on a more literal meaning. Dr Donald Gould, former editor of *World Medicine,* and currently editor of the *New Scientist,* declares: 'The pattern of advance of medical technology suggests that before too long we may have to decree that the various pumps, potions and prostheses which can keep a man alive beyond his natural span should be withdrawn when he reaches some statutory age.'

A friend in need

Some of the most agonizing ethical problems will certainly be raised by the recent discovery – reported in 1967 – that life can be saved by joining together the blood circulation of a diseased organism with that of a healthy one. A three-man team at the Bio-Research Institute in Cambridge, Massachusetts, joined Syrian hamsters suffering from an inherited heart disease to healthy hamsters. The diseased animals belonged to an inbred strain known as BIO 14.6, which develops congestive heart failure at the age of about 90 days and dies of it by the age of 150 days. On autopsy, they show fluid retention and congestion of the liver, lungs and other organs, just as in human heart failure. Moreover their retention of fluid responds to the same treatment as is used to treat human heart failure, so it is reasonable to conclude that we can learn about human heart disease by studying these animals.

The team found that the diseased animals thus joined to healthy animals (this joining is known as parabiosis) lived much longer than would otherwise have been the case. In particular, the tendency to develop swellings due to fluid retention was abolished. The disease itself was not arrested, but the experiment suggests that hormones from the healthy animal were able to cope with the fluid retention in the diseased animal.

Attempts, premature as some people might think, have been made by several Canadian medical men to use a similar technique on human patients. Thus in 1965 in Seattle, at the University of Washington School of Medicine, a woman suffering from kidney disease was connected to a man suffering from cancer, on the argument that each might help the other. The kidneys of the man with cancer would help flush out the waste products which the diseased kidneys of the second patient could not eliminate. Conversely, the latter patient's immune system might manufacture antibodies against the cancer of her cosufferer. In point of fact, both patients died in short order.

However, the kidney patient was considerably helped: she was roused from coma, during the fifty hours of crosscirculation, and died during convalescence from a bleeding ulcer. The cancer patient incurred some jaundice from the waste products of the other patient's liver. In another case, the kidney patient was improved to the point where a transplant was possible (though she died later from an infection of the wound). Here her 'parabiosee' was a leukemic patient; in another such case the kidney patient has not (after one year) shown any signs of leukemia, though the leukemic patient was not saved.

The ethics of such experiments seem dubious, at this stage of medical knowledge, since it seems at least equally probable that the two patients would harm one another. The general health of the cancer patient must surely have been lowered by the presence of additional waste products, if not actual toxins, in his blood. And since the presence of toxins in the blood of cancer patients has been demonstrated, it is even more probable that he harmed his fellow.

The parabiosis of two sick people seems to me likely to offer advantages only in some special cases: for instance, a person with a low level of output of some hormone might be joined for a time to a person with unduly high output, to the advantage of both. This might help to overcome a temporary set-back, such as post-operative shock. The parabiosis of a diseased and a healthy person is another story, though it has some parallels with the case of the healthy person who donates a kidney. There are many respects in which nature provides a margin, and it is highly probable a healthy person could produce enough hormones, antibodies and other physiological substances to make up the lack in a diseased person. In this way, a healthy person might postpone indefinitely the death of an ill person – at the cost no doubt of having to remain permanently in bed alongside his parabiosee.

I cannot conceive a doctor asking anyone to make such a sacrifice in the ordinary way, though I can conceive that some people might feel a strong sense of obligation to give such help, believing that if death could be postponed, some means of cure might one day be found. In war or time of crisis, too, there might be strong motivation to sustain the life of a great leader, or a scientist in charge of a major project (one thinks of the atomic bomb project in the last great war). In an authoritarian country, it might well be represented to people that it was their duty to serve the nation in such a way, sacrificing perhaps a month of their life and then giving place to another volunteer.

There is also the dilemma which may face the doctor or surgeon who initiates parabiosis as a temporary measure and then finds that he cannot terminate it without condemning the weaker partner to death. Is he then entitled to sacrifice the weaker for the benefit of the stronger? Should he discuss the situation with the victim and obtain his consent? And what if this consent were emphatically refused? And yet again, perhaps the stronger person might refuse the responsibility of sacrificing his blood-brother. One can even imagine a wealthy person offering financial inducements to such a service, and while few people might sacrifice their freedom for money simply in their own interests, they might wish to do so to help a child or relative.

Up to now, such questions have scarcely been debated, let alone answered.

There is yet one more way in which life might be prolonged – perhaps indefinitely – which exceeds in *hubris* anything I have so far described.

Severed heads

It was in 1963 that the world first became aware of the experiments which Dr Robert J. White of the Cleveland Metropolitan General Hospital had been conducting, together with his co-workers – experiments which, twenty years before, had been described in science fiction and mocked as absurd and impossible exaggerations. After five years' work, this medical team had managed to remove a monkey's brain from its skull and keep it alive on an artificial circulation for seven hours. Recordings of the electrical activity of this isolated brain were at first approximately normal, and the fact that it was consuming oxygen and releasing carbon dioxide into the circulating blood seemed to prove that the brain was still alive.

Soon after, three Wisconsin surgeons reported similar experiments in which fifteen dogs were decapitated and their brains were kept alive. Even at this stage, some concern for the ethics of this work began to manifest itself. The *New Scientist* observed that the surgeons seemed to have considered the possibility that the still living brains of these animals might appreciate pain because they had applied a local anaesthetic to the exposed tissues of the neck, and added: 'but physical pain is not the only agony a disembodied brain could suffer. There is urgent need for biologists to evolve a policy to regulate such experiments.'

By 1966 these experiments had been carried a stage or two further. First, the Cleveland team, finding that blood tended to be damaged by the heart-machine they were using, developed a technique for removing the brains, cooling them to 2° or 3° C for several hours, and then joining them to the circulatory system of a second dog. These brains they also showed to be alive by monitoring their electrical activity and chemical turnover. These heads they kept 'alive' for periods up to two days.

In stage two, the team removed entire heads and maintained them in this way, noting that the pupils of the eyes contracted when light was shone on them and that there was a 'rhythmic gasping'. They concluded: 'These findings demonstrated not only that the individual nerve cells in the brain were alive, but that, in part at least, the brains were functioning as whole organs.' The electrical activity of these brains was maintained for six hours, but after twelve hours there was in no case any electrical response.

In the experiments the recipient dogs were 'either maintained in a state of light anaesthesia or were allowed to awaken'. Were their brains conscious? Dr White argues that consciousness almost certainly depends on the reception of signals from many parts of the body and that, with these cut out, consciousness as we know it is unlikely to occur. This is by no means the general view of psychologists.

Dr Peter Stubbs, reviewing his work in the *New Scientist*, held that 'this kind of guess is scarcely good enough. The mechanism and nature of consciousness is hardly understood at all and the nightmarish situation that, even remotely, could arise within a disembodied brain leaves little latitude for such experiments.'

In 1966 Dr White visited Great Britain and while there he was interviewed on television by Dr Donald Gould, then the editor of *World Medicine*. He revealed that the duration of these experiments was now being extended to days by the new technique of using the circulatory system of other animals to support the brain. Dr Gould asked him the question which must have been uppermost in the minds of many who heard about this work: would it be possible to maintain a human brain in this way? Dr White replied: 'There is no question that this is within the capability of laboratories today.' He added that this would actually be easier than maintaining monkey brains, since fully developed heart-lung apparatus for human beings was already in existence. Asked whether this was not a horrifying idea, he said: 'Having talked to religious groups about this, I have been surprised that they were not more condemning.' By the nineties or the end of the century, he added, 'the idea won't seem so overwhelming.'

Donald Gould returned to the main question again before the end of the interview, and Dr White repeated: 'The possibility of maintaining a human brain is definitely there,' but added that he did not himself consider attempting such an experiment because of the 'social implications'. Whether he meant, by this, the criticism he might attract, or compunction of his own, or such wider questions as whether, when a body is faced with death, there might be a moral obligation to maintain the individual personality as long as possible, he did not explain.

If one's first reaction to such experiments is one of horror, it is important to bear in mind that they may have important consequences for brain surgery. They make clear that the brain is a far less fragile organ than has been commonly supposed, and indicate that far more radical brain surgery than any we now attempt may be possible. Perhaps one can visualize the day when complete sections of brain damaged by a tumour or hemorrhage could be replaced – especially since there is no immune reaction in brain tissue. However, the sacrifice of animals for experimental purposes is a commonplace, though some countries insist that no pain be caused in so doing.

It is on the human plane that the most profound problems arise. Once such a technique is established, the situation will surely arise that individuals, faced with death or even paralysis or intractable pain, may demand to be kept 'alive' in such a manner. It could even be argued that doctors have an obligation to prolong lives in this way.

Moreover, the surgeon who, having once sustained such a brain, allows it to die, could be regarded as having committed murder. So, if the number of brains thus maintained became considerable, public authorities might find themselves saddled with the novel burden of guaranteeing their support.

As the *New Scientist* observed, 'It is right that we should pause and consider the long-term implications of the notable technical achievement that Dr White reports. What dreams may come to a disembodied brain, and what pain, that the mute organ is unable to express? How far along this road does consciousness and individuality persist, and at what point is the owner of the brain deemed to be dead?' Then it raised the question whether such experiments should be allowed to continue:

> Where, between the present experiments and the long-range possibility of attempts to preserve an active human mind in a bottle, should we say 'Stop!'? We must remember, too, that here is only one more instance of a remarkable flowering of techniques of many kinds, ranging from prosthetics to chromosomal manipulations, which have tremendous potential for good, but also allow a mockery of nature.

But these may be only the most immediate issues raised by such work. For it may be that improved tissue-culture techniques will make it possible to grow complete brains from fragments of nervous tissue, while the development of electronics and prosthetics may make it possible to fit them with organs of speech, or these could be transplanted at the same time as the brain, as happens in whole-head transplantation. Eyes and ears they can retain even more simply. Thus we may face the day when we can talk to a brain derived by purely artificial means and discover whether it differs in any material, or immaterial, respect from our own.

Immortality?

How much weight, in the light of all this, can we attach to the prospect of actual immortality?

The idea is by no means ridiculous, though many people tend to think so. Death is an evolutionary rather than a biological necessity. Some primitive creatures are virtually immortal. Perhaps the nearest thing we know to an immortal among the more complex creatures is found among the jellyfishes. The jellyfish are produced from a stub known as a schyphistoma larva, and, though each animal has a limited life, the stub appears to carry on indefinitely. Thus cumulative cell death is not inevitable. Death became part of life's plan because evolution favours creatures that die, provided that they die after the reproductive age is passed. For then the species can be modified by natural selection to meet changing conditions. Creatures which lived for ever but did not reproduce would slowly become obsolete. As Sir George Pickering has put it: 'In so far as man is an improvement on monkeys, this is due to death. . . . A new species, for better or worse, can only start with a new life.'

Even if cell death cannot be wholly prevented, the replacement of wornout parts by implantation techniques may provide an indefinite possibility of life extension. It is the prevention of senility which, as we have seen, represents the real problem.

The social consequences of immortality, however, would be so serious that it would be disastrous to make use of such an achievement, except by way of rarest exception. For if people live for ever (or even very long) the population must rise explosively, unless all procreation ceases – and it is inconceivable that the human race should abandon procreation, a practice to which it is impelled by such strong instincts and from which it derives emotional rewards. Indeed, the very cohesion of society may depend on the lessons learned within the childparent relationship. In any case, we obviously know virtually nothing about the sociology of a society, or even a very large social group, composed predominantly and increasingly of old people – old in experience, in cynicism, in blaséness, if not old in tissues and metabolism.

Once we bestow on man the power to extend life indefinitely, we place in a new perspective the contrary possibility: the power to end life.

As a young man, I once went to see an old lady of 108. She had been bed-ridden for 23 years and lived on the charity of a grandchild, whose only spare room she occupied. After chatting a while she suddenly burst out: 'Why can't I die? Why doesn't God take me away? I'm a burden to my grandchild and a burden to myself. I just lie here all day and pray for death.' There are others who, by the age of 60 or so, begin to find life tasteless and boring. In tradition, the punishment visited on the betrayer of Jesus, the Wandering Jew, was immortality. Who knows what it feels like to be even 150?

As long as longevity is bestowed by a special treatment, he who finds life tasteless can always ignore the treatment. The extension of life due to medical intervention cannot be thus ignored, and we have already seen how 'life machines' can impose a sort of 'forced living'. I conclude that we shall have to change our attitudes to suicide and euthanasia. This does not necessarily mean a wholesale derestriction of suicide. The possibility of applying for a licence to die can also be considered.

But, as Dr Murray Tondon of Stanford University has pointed out, certain people are natural assets, and the state – some regimes – may be reluctant to allow its most brilliant scientist, administrator or even artist to depart from the scene. The attempt to die, despite the efforts of those who would keep one alive, might form the most macabre of dramas, and the right to die may one day need to be defended as the most fundamental of human liberties.

5
New Minds for Old

'Everyone complains of his memory,' said the French wit la Roche-
foucauld, 'but no one complains of his judgment.' However, most people
would like to be able to improve both, and it looks as if they may be able
to. Whether it will make mankind any happier is much less certain.

We stand on the threshold of a new era in understanding the mind,
and more than one scientist has expressed the opinion that the biggest area
of advance in biology during the next half-century may be that of neurophysiology. Three major areas of excitement and progress can be detected
among the numerous enquiries in the field. First, there is a growing power
to intervene in the non-intellectual functions of the brain: a growing
ability to alter moods and emotional states – a development which is
based on the realization that the brain is not simply an electrical or com-
puter-like mechanism, but a complex chemical system as well. Secondly,
a spirit of extreme optimism has sprung up concerning the possibility of
discovering the nature of memory. Finally, there is a guarded belief that
one may be able to effect considerable improvements in the level of
intelligence of future generations, even if the idea of an 'intelligence pill'
which turns us all into geniuses in a week or two remains chimerical.

Ten years ago, Professor Jean Rostand foresaw the extraordinary
significance of the early work on mood-control (as we may call it) and
with Gallic wit declared: 'Special hormones or other chemical agents
will be used to reinforce the vigour of a man's mind, to strengthen his
character, to dispose him to virtuousness. Quite soon, perhaps, people
will buy genius or sanctity at the chemist's just as now women buy the
straightness of their nose or the depth of their gaze at the beauty parlour.'

It does not require much imagination to see that the power to regulate morality by drugs would raise unique ethical problems, and might change our whole system of life – politics, economics, war, the lot – even if we leave aside the probability that such powers would be misused. Equally, if we could shift levels of intelligence, the whole pattern of competitive interpersonal behaviour would be transformed, while if everyone were more intelligent, many of the precautions which we take against folly would become unnecessary. On the other hand, if only a minority acquire heightened intelligence, an élite system might develop which would put paid to democracy as most people now understand it. Yet again, if powers of memory can be greatly improved – still more, if ready-made memories can be bestowed – the whole educational system, based as it is largely on cramming in facts, will have to be re-oriented.

And these three areas, mood, intelligence and memory, are merely the three currently most active fields: there are other areas of research still in a more exploratory stage which might, in due time, have just as dramatic an influence on our lives.

If the effects of the advance in biological understanding of the working of the body are disturbing, the effects of discovering in detail how the brain works are likely to be positively alarming. Society is adjusted to the basic facts of human mental attainment and weakness in many intricate ways. Any drastic change in parameters such as intelligence, memory-power, emotionality or ability to take decisions would create problems for which there is literally no precedent. And if such knowledge lent increased power to those who might misuse it to influence or control others, might not undreamed-of tyrannies arise?

It therefore seems worth looking rather closely at the state of play in this field in order to see whether the optimism (if that is the right word) of the research scientists is justified; and, if so, just where and how soon society had better begin preparing for the consequences.

To medieval man it was inconceivable that the brain, this few pounds of sloppy jelly, could perform the functions of thought and feeling, of decision and memory. It was easier to think of it as an anchorage point for some invisible soul or spirit, which would execute these functions, handing down the orders to the body to behave accordingly. Some, indeed, denied the brain responsibility for thought at all, and placed the seat of reason in the stomach. And that the feelings were located in the heart was a commonplace, as popular expressions in many languages show.

Perhaps the g eatest breakthrough which has occurred in this century is the realization that the brain is a perfectly adequate device for thought; how it handles emotions and memory is less obvious, but the fact it does is now undoubted, and the structures within the brain which do so are now being investigated.

What has made its reasoning functions credible is the invention of the computer: a device consisting of thousands of identical switches, intricately wired together. The anatomists of the nineteenth century, like the Spaniard Ramon y Cajal, demonstrated that the brain consists not of thousands, but of hundreds of millions of inter-connected neurones, and these were later shown to be switches – rather fancy switches, but nevertheless switches. The way in which electric signals are transmitted through this system has become clear, though the details of the circuitry are only just beginning to be unravelled. The brain, whatever else it is besides, is certainly a very sophisticated computer. Or, as W. Nauta once said, it is four computers connected together. One monitors input, and filters out the trivial. One is an automatic pilot, executing all habitual functions. One is a calculating machine – and this is a double set of equipment, perhaps for the same reason that airline booking is often executed with double-banked equipment. It also appears to be the seat of memory. The last computer is concerned in some ill-understood way with feelings, and with primitive needs like hunger, thirst and sex.

The second new insight about the brain, and this one is only a decade or so old, is that the brain is also a complex chemical device. Its parts respond in subtle ways to the influence of substances in the fluids which bathe them, and contain specialized chemical agents – gangliosides, cerebrosides, sphingomyelin and so on – the functions of which are still obscure. Moreover, some brain cells secrete controlling substances, or neurohumours, which stimulate or calm other parts of the brain. To Sherrington, the great neurophysiologist who died in 1952, the brain was a vast electrical switchboard, and in the years between the wars his successors were busy trying to understand it in purely electrical terms, stimulating it electrically and measuring the electrical waves it produced.

Today, physiologists are busy dripping chemicals into it through fine

tubes, analysing the substances in it and their distribution, and synthesiz/
ing a growing range of drugs which, when they reach it through the
bloodstream, affect its functioning.

Each new approach reveals the brain as more complex than was
thought previously, and it may well be fifty years or more before its mode
of working is understood in any depth. But one does not have to under/
stand a thing completely to be able to influence it, and the first/fruits of
these new insights will ripen quite soon. Indeed, some of them have
already been gathered. The somewhat superficial and fumbling research
which is now going on has already yielded new techniques of practical
importance and none more so than in the field of mood control.

Mood control

Of course, influencing affective states by chemical means is an old trick.
Early in civilization man found he could use alcohol for this purpose,
and chewed ivy and other plants for their effect on his mind. Berserk rage
was probably induced in this way. Aphrodisiac smells and potions must
have been discovered very early and the anaphrodisiac effect of some of
these natural drugs has long been noted. Thus in the Yemen, a substance
prepared from the buds or leaves of the plant *Catha edulis* is sold widely.
It excites the central nervous system, producing gaiety and banishing
hunger, but it also dulls desire and leads, if used frequently, to cardiac
disorders. Or again in Gabon, iboga, derived from *Tabernanthe iboga*, is
chewed to banish fatigue. It contains two alkaloids of unknown structure,
christened ibogaine and iboganine, which have never been properly in/
vestigated.

The possibility of controlling our moods was thus always at hand, and
it is perhaps surprising that it is only recently that it has been put on a
scientific footing.

It was in 1947 that Professor Robert Robinson, a distinguished British
chemist, asked the Swiss drug firm of CIBA if they could make ajmaline
for him, and it was not until 1952 that they succeeded. Interest in ajmaline
had been aroused by the use in India of the powdered root of *Rauwolfia*,
known as sarpaganda, to combat heart disease; the active principle was
found to be ajmaline. But besides reducing blood pressure it appeared to
have a general calming effect on the patient. Soon, Dr Nathan Kline of

the Rockland State Hospital, New York, tried using it to help psychotics, and got good results. At first his reports were greeted with scorn: insanity, psychiatrists said, was the product of childhood experience and not to be fought off with drugs. But in fact what Kline had pounced on was the first of the ataractics or, as they are now generally known, the tranquillizers.

The last twenty years have seen the emergence of three important groups of drugs acting on the mind: the analeptics or stimulants, such as pipradol, which counter depression and often act to produce a state of euphoria, or well-being, and do so without reducing appetite or interfering with sleep; the muscle-relaxants and tranquillizers, like chlorpromazine and meprobomate; and the hallucinogens, of which LSD-25 is known almost too well. In addition, we now have anti-convulsants for epilepsy: trimethadione for petit mal and diphenyl-hydantoin for grand mal.

Tranquillizers, it should be added, do more than sooth the nerves of harassed business men. In large doses, they calm frantic psychotics; in smaller ones they can make elderly patients more alert, active and co-operative. Variant forms, like methimazole, slow down the frenzied activity of the hyperthyroid patient, or like azacyclonal, block the psychotic episodes sometimes produced by LSD-25.

It would be absurd to suppose, however, that the discovery of new mind drugs will stop at this point. As the chemistry of the brain is gradually unravelled, an increasingly extensive and precise intervention in mood will surely become possible.

At present, the action of such drugs is often inconsistent and un-reliable. They often produce startling effects in a minority of subjects, some effect in a majority and none at all in a few. Why this is so is a mystery. Moreover, their effect on psychotics and on normal people can be widely different. A dose of tranquillizer, such as chlorpromazine, which would calm a schizophrenic, improving his thinking and quelling his hallucinations, would leave a normal person numb, fatigued and miser-able. We are not yet in a position to engineer drugs with precisely the effects we want; but that is clearly the end state towards which present research is tending.

We may actually be on the way to banishing insanity. The success which has already been achieved with schizophrenia and the depressions is not always appreciated by the layman. Until twelve years ago, the figures of admission of mental cases were rising steadily. Then, following the introduction of the new drugs, they began to turn down for the first time in many years.

How far schizophrenia has a chemical cause is still a matter of warm controversy: there are those like Dr H. Osmond of the Princeton Neuro-psychiatric Service's Divisional Research Center, who says emphatically that it has. The older school are sceptical. Recently, a new drug, huphen-azine enanthate, injected every two to four weeks, has been found to control the symptoms of schizophrenia for up to four weeks. The way things are going, it looks as if soon we shall be able not only to drive men mad with drugs, but also to drive them sane.

No longer will people be happy or sad, amiable or aggressive, active or lazy, calm or anxious, merely because it was their nature or because circumstances evoked the mood; they will be so because they took the appropriate pill. Humanists may feel that there is a personal loss involved in evading the various moods which life experiences bring us. Human beings protected from genuine emotion may be in some sense impover-ished. Against this, it could be argued that even the most cloistered and unadventurous individuals will be able to experience pinnacles of emotion they would never otherwise have known – the rapture of gazing on a new ocean for the first time, the utter abandonment of the dark night of the soul. Such individuals might be richer, better able to appreciate the feelings of others, thanks to having had similar experiences themselves.

Socially, however, it may be disturbing not to know for sure if a person is genuinely himself. We feel some awkwardness in dealing with the intoxicated man, and still more in dealing with the insane, because society does not provide us with adequate conventions of behaviour. Insults which we would resent from a sober man, for instance, we may feel bound to ignore from a drunk. When a psychotic tries to persuade us to a course of action, we remain wary. When we try to reason with the psychotic and find our arguments produce action quite other than we intended, we feel baffled and impotent. It is probably this which is the main factor in the common objection to the use of behaviour-changing drugs.

Indeed, if the experience of the past few years is a guide, society will be prompt to prohibit the use of most of these drugs, except on a doctor's prescription. The tranquillizers, once sold freely, have been restricted in this way. The hallucinogens, although relatively harmless, have also been banned.

Among the arguments advanced to justify such bans have been that various disturbances of behaviour result – even that people may drive cars under their influence, and become involved in accidents. But of course this is also true of alcohol, which we do not ban: we restrict the freedom of young people to consume it, and we make special regulations to cover cases, such as car driving, where the safety of others may be affected. The readiness with which society has acted against non-addictive personality-changing drugs reflects, I suspect, rather deep unconscious anxieties concerning such matters. The fact that we are so slow to prohibit many more dangerous and even lethal substances suggests that our motives are less pure than they look.

Recently, Dr Heinz Lehmann of McGill University forecast the discovery of a drug which would dissipate aggression: an 'anti-aggression pill'. A drug of this kind would present a further set of ethical and social problems. He probably had in mind the work of Seegmiller, Rosenbloom and Kelley at the National Institute of Arthritis and Mental Disease. This team showed that over-production of uric acid can occur as the result of the absence of a certain enzyme (hypoxanthine-guanine-phos-phoribosyl-transferase) though only in males. It is well established that too much uric acid causes compulsive aggressive behaviour and also results in mental retardation. It may well be that other disturbances in body chemistry are also associated with extreme irritability – the tetchiness of the gouty man is already proverbial.

It is not clear that such irritability is aggression in the strict sense; aggression is normally defined as an attempt to dominate others in order to achieve a sense of security, and sometimes as a form of revenge for remembered insults or deprivations. (The question is quite complex, but we need not analyse aggression in detail here.) To dissolve aggression of this type may call for therapies of a different type – perhaps even the dissolving of old, painful memories by the techniques discussed in the following section.

It is reasonable to assume, however, that at least in *some* cases it may be possible to banish aggression. The ethical question therefore arises whether society would be justified in compelling aggressive persons to take such

NEW MINDS FOR OLD

treatment. Is this not a form of brain-washing? The answer must be yes, but at the same time the case is not very different from that of the manic-depressive psychotic who is given electroshock or who undergoes lobotomy. Society's problem is to decide when a man is dangerous enough to treat in this way. Up to now it has avoided treating anyone who was not directly physically violent. The person who expressed his aggression more deviously was and is exempt.

There is also a moral issue, raised by Anthony Burgess in his most unusual novel *The Clockwork Orange*. In it, a delinquent who obtains sexual excitement from violence, destructiveness and rape is conditioned to feel sick at the sight of violence. He becomes meek and fawning, offers to turn the other cheek. Is there any value, Burgess asks by implication, in virtuous behaviour which is not based on moral effort and moral choice? The boy has become a 'clockwork orange' – a simulacrum of the organic reality, with only crude mechanisms inside.

The scientist who sees organic life as based on mechanisms which differ from clockwork only by being immensely more complex will not be impressed by this image. But he should not dismiss the issue which Burgess raises because of this. Even without bringing in mystical, vitalistic assumptions about the nature of personality, it is still perfectly justifiable to say that the mechanisms which guide choice in a normal human being are so much more complex than the kind of simple conditioned response imposed on Burgess's anti-hero as to be greatly preferable in human terms. (To be sure there are scientists who do not recognize this fact. In particular, Professor H. J. Eysenck has hotly advocated the wider use of just such operant conditioning techniques for a long time, and in the U.S.A. they have recently become known through the work of Dr J. Wolpé and others.)

Either way, as 'moral' behaviour becomes controllable, new problems will arise in penology and law. The British Lord Chancellor, Lord Gardiner, not long since attributed the large number of men in jail to 'lack of moral judgment'. On the other hand, Dr W. M. Court Brown at Edinburgh showed not long ago that a significant proportion of anti-social persons possessed hereditary chromosomal defects – implying that their behaviour was, at least to some extent, the consequence of their imperfect physical development and to that extent not their 'fault' at all. The two assessments are not necessarily as far apart from each other as might seem to be the case. Most psychologists would agree that 'moral judgment' results from an appropriate sequence of learning experiences in early life and is also dependent on adequate emotional development. It can readily be shown in monkeys that deprivation in infancy restricts emotional development and leads to impoverished personal relationships.

It is becoming ever clearer that social behaviour derives from mechanisms which are understandable and therefore controllable. The familiar issue, that all crime is too readily excused on psychiatric grounds, is bound to become still more familiar, until society tires of trying to deal with crime by punishment, or even by rehabilitation after the event, and turns to mending the conditions which cause the distorted psychic development which manifests as 'lack of moral judgment'.

Lastly, a further set of moral problems would arise if a ruler or leader began to make use of mood-controlling drugs for political purposes. Thus he might feed aggression pills to his soldiers and airmen (for if it is possible to make anti-aggression pills it must be possible to make pro-aggression pills also) and anti-aggression pills and euphoriants to the public who might unseat him. The possibility that police forces might be equipped with anti-aggression sprays, in place of the hoses and tear gas which they now use, should be taken quite seriously,

But before discussing these wider issues, it will be as well to consider some other aspects of mind control, notably the growing understanding of the nature of memory and intelligence.

Memory lane

Current research into the nature of memory is in a highly controversial stage; nevertheless, it holds out the possibility of improvement of recall and the definite probability that erasure of memory may, in certain circumstances, be possible. It even hints at the weird prospect of being able to inject memories or of being able to transfer memories from one person to another after they have been formed.

What we loosely call memory comprises three distinct processes: read-in, storage and recall. The information must be entered in the filing system, must not fade or be destroyed while in it, and must be traceable when wanted. As anyone who has ever used a filing system knows, it is the third stage which gives most trouble. When we say that we have a poor memory, it is usually because we cannot bring something to mind when we want it. Nevertheless, we know that we know it, and afterwards, when it is too late, it often comes back to us.

If we receive a blow on the head, we may 'lose our memory' – suffer from amnesia – but later the memories return, and it is a curious fact that they return in the reverse order to that in which they were formed; the most recent are recovered first. It is almost as if they were buried layer upon layer. Clearly the filing system has remained intact: it is the much more vulnerable recovery system which has broken down.

Currently, scientists are preoccupied with the question of how memories are stored: once this is known it should be easier to investigate how they are read-in and recovered. The current air of optimism is due to the belief that the answer to the main question is in sight, and this optimism tends, I think, to obscure the fact that the other two questions remain almost wholly baffling.

A few years ago, when the brain was conceived of primarily as an electric machine, the popular line was that the storage was electrical. Since some early computers used resonating circuits as memory devices, it was thought that the brain might do the same. A succession of pulses, carrying information in much the same way that the Morse code does, would circle endlessly round a loop, to be tapped when required.

Then, when the development of molecular biology made it clear that information could be embodied in long-chain molecules, the idea was soon advanced that memory might be stored in molecules too, and was widely taken up.

It was Professor Holger Hydén of Gothenburg University in Sweden who, in 1961, first popularized this notion, saying that RNA was in fact the molecule in question. Analysing the brains of rats which had been trained in sundry tasks, he found not only increased quantities of RNA present, but a change in its composition.

The idea that the ultimate nature of memory is chemical, rather than electrical, is strongly supported by the fact the memories remain unimpaired after the brain's electrical activity has been temporarily stopped by cold, shock, drugs and many other kinds of stress. We have, however, a short-term memory – the one we employ in holding a telephone number while we dial it – which may well be electrical in nature.

Most such memories vanish rapidly, which is just as well, as we should be swamped by the mass of irrelevant detail, and should have difficulty finding the information we wanted among it. There are a number of experiments with animals which suggest that it takes some hours before a memory-trace is printed into long-term memory. They suggest, more-over, that the trace is held at first in an electrical form, but is finally embodied in a chemical form for permanent storage.

Only storage at the molecular level seems able to explain the vast capacity which man has for data. It has been estimated that, for a com-puter to have a memory rivalling a man's, it would require an area of magnetic tape equal to the entire surface of the earth. 'Molecular neuro-logy' is the still unfamiliar label which Francis O. Schmitt of MIT has coined for this new-born specialism.

The chemical approach to memory soon received strong support from the experiments of two young graduate students at the University of Texas. In the early 1950's, Robert Thompson and James V. McConnell began to carry out some experiments on memory that have since become widely known, not to say famous, and which have given a new impetus to research on memory. They chose as their research subject not human beings or higher mammals, as had most of their predecessors, but a lowly wormlike creature found in ditch-water and known as a planarian. In an evolutionary sense, it is the simplest creature to have anything which could reasonably be called a brain – a network of some 400 cells. But planarians are also the most complex of the creatures which can divide by fission. Cut one in half and not only will the head grow a new tail, but the tail will grow a new head.

Thompson and McConnell shone a bright light on each planarian; several seconds later it received a mild electric shock. The light merely caused it to stretch itself. The shock caused it to contract or to turn its head. After a hundred or so repetitions of this light/shock experience, the planarians usually started to contract when the light stimulus alone was given. Apparently, they had *learned* that light meant: 'shock coming'. The scientific world was sceptical: such a simple creature could not be expected to learn anything. Actually, an animal which receives a barrage of stimuli is irritated into a hypersensitive state, and this confuses the issue, as experimenters who had tried to 'condition' planaria forty years before found. Thompson and McConnell avoided this trap by requiring (a) that a planarian respond at least 23 times in every 25 tests, and (b) that, after it had been allowed to 'forget' the experience, it should relearn in fewer trials than previously.

The next step was to cut the trained planarians in half and let them regenerate. It was then found that not only did the head-half relearn in fewer trials than before, but the tail-half did also! How had the memory been preserved in the half which did not have a brain?

As I have mentioned, the idea had already been advanced by Holger Hydén that memory might be stored in the molecules of RNA, in much the same way that genetic information is stored in DNA. So William C. Corning of the University of Rochester, having cut his trained planarians in half, allowed them to regenerate in a solution of ribonuclease, an enzyme which specifically destroys RNA. He found that, whereas the head-half planarians still showed enhanced ability to relearn their lesson, the tail-halves had forgotten. This did not prove that RNA carried the memory. It could be that ribonuclease cannot get into head-halves, or that it destroyed the mechanism by which the tail-half put the memory back into the new head. But it did make RNA look very interesting in the context of memory.

Subsequently, the teams performed many other experiments which revealed the difficulty of interpreting planarian behaviour. At times it seemed as though the planarian was merely thrown into a state of anxiety, or hyper-irritability, rather than that it had learned in the strict sense of the word. The most sensational result of all was that in which planarians of a cannibalistic breed ate the chopped-up bodies of trained worms and then themselves showed enhanced learning power. Had they actually acquired the memories of the worms they ate? Professors of psychology, half seriously, envisaged the day when their class would learn their subject by eating their teachers.

That the molecules had survived the digestive processes seemed possible in planarians, improbable in higher organisms.

The destruction of memories and also their transfer to other organisms had thus been achieved, if McConnell's experiments were sound, at least in a lowly organism. A Californian team attempted to repeat this work, using more planarians, more kinds of stimuli and longer testing intervals. They reported negative results, but McConnell replied, in effect, that they lacked skill in handling planarians, and that other workers had repeated his experiments with success.

Experiments such as those described do not prove conclusively that RNA is the repository of memory. It seems slightly more likely, on the face of it, that memory should be embodied in specific proteins, and it is known that nerve cells manufacture proteins faster than other cells. The RNA may simply play an intermediary role in this process.

If you remove parts of the brain of an animal, you seem to impoverish its memory in a general way, rather than to eliminate specific memories, and it makes little difference which parts of the cortex you remove. It has several times been suggested that memories are diffused throughout the brain, and depend on the setting of innumerable 'switches'. If so, the function of the proteins made by the nerve cells may simply be to act as switches. If so, memory is *both* chemical *and* electrical, a solution which appeals to me as inherently probable.

It was in the early sixties that analogous experiments began to be conducted with mammals. Dr Allan Jacobson (a former colleague of McConnell's) and co-workers at the University of California taught a number of animals, chiefly rats and hamsters, a task – to go to a feeding box when a light flashed or when a click was heard – then killed them and extracted the RNA from their brains. This was then injected into un- trained rats which showed, not indeed an immediate grasp of the lesson, but a reduced learning time. Objectors said that RNA had merely acted as a stimulant. In a similar manner, Unger and Oceguera-Navaño at Baylor University habituated rats to noise and claimed to have transferred the tolerance to other rats. Jacobson also introduced a new note when he injected RNA from trained hamsters into rats and claimed that their learning performance was improved too.

Can memory cross the species barrier? Is memory based on identical coding throughout the whole range of living creatures? It seems that the coding for protein synthesis is basically the same, throughout the animal kingdom, so it was not inherently unlikely that memory would also be universal. Would-be humorists asked whether it was wise, any longer, to eat calves' brains.

Meanwhile, progress was also being made with the destruction of memories. Dr Bernard W. Agranoff, at Michigan University's Mental Health Research Institute, started from the fact that the antibiotic puro- mycin has the power of preventing the formation of protein. Using gold- fish as his experimental animals, he taught them to ring a bell in order to obtain food, a trick which the Japanese sometimes teach their fish for fun. Then, at various stages in the process, he injected puromycin into their brains. When it was injected some hours after the conditioning process, it had no effect. Presumably the memory-proteins were already formed. But if it was injected just before the lesson, or even soon after, the lesson was not learned.

There are also substances which prevent the synthesis of RNA itself, such as 8-azaguanine, and they too cause impairment of learning if injected just before, but the dose has to be so high as to be almost lethal. Nevertheless, such experiments must be regarded as putting memory-erasure very much into the realm of possibility. Once the way has been shown, the rest is development.

It is not difficult to visualize a political use, or misuse, of the power of erasing memories as soon as they have been formed, or of preventing them forming. Indeed, when a reporter asked Dr Agranoff whether the Central Intelligence Agency had been in touch with him about his work, he replied with a smile, 'I forget'. However, in these experiments the puromycin was injected directly into the brain, and in doses so massive as to be lethal if continued. This clearly rules out its use on human beings. But once the principle is established, the prospect opens up that one day someone may find a substance which can be introduced into the blood-stream by injection, or even swallowed, which will have the same effect. So the erasure of memory is a possibility which must be taken quite seriously.

Are we also to infer from experiments of this kind that memory can, or could, be transferred from one human being to another? No scientist, I suppose, would risk a definite forecast. In my opinion, provided it is quite definitely established that memory is encoded into molecules, there is a definite likelihood that, one day – probably quite a long time ahead – some degree of memory transfer may be effected. I do not foresee that students will ever be tempted to eat their teachers, like those tribesmen who eat their enemies in order to acquire their virtue; I should be sur-prised if the memory molecules would, first, survive the digestive processes. Nor am I convinced that they would reach the brain, even if in-jected into the bloodstream. There is an ill-understood protective mechan-ism, known as the blood-brain barrier, which guards the brain, to some extent, from circulating debris. It has not been shown that RNA, at all events, can cross this barrier. However, with the advance of knowledge, ways of temporarily abrogating the barrier may conceivably be developed. Even so, memory will hardly be sold in cans, like soup.

Success may come, more probably, by developing techniques currently used to drip fluids directly into the cavities within the brain, or on to its surface – but this involves drilling a hole through the skull. Finally, we do not know for sure that molecules, even when they reach the surface of a brain cell, will be admitted and there take their place alongside existing memory molecules without disturbance. The implication of the memory-transfer experiments is that they will. This work, therefore, calls for close attention.

The social implications of effective memory transfer would be almost too extraordinary to conceive. Firstly, education would be radically affected. The examination papers which ask the student to name the parts of a plant, or list the battles in a war, would become obsolete. Whether a student knew certain facts or not would depend entirely on whether his parents or teachers had chosen to have them injected. Tests would have to become, as many people already think they should anyway, tests of what a student can do with his knowledge.* Correspondingly, lectures and 'mugging up the answers' generally would become obsolete. And no doubt, by this time, the availability of computer memories will have made rote-learning even less useful.

The learning of foreign languages might become simple, and the world may finally escape from the confusion created at Babel. However, the pressure to standardize a small number of languages, thus reducing the cost of acquiring the ability to converse freely with no matter whom, may increase.

In place of the numerous class-rooms and lecture-rooms of today will the school need only a surgical suite? and pupils, instead of spending ten years of their life sitting in these rooms, pass only a few days in the school hospital?

If memories can be acquired then probably skills can be acquired also,

* 'Open-book examinations', in which the student can consult any reference sources he wishes while preparing the answers required by the paper, have been tried by some western universities and schools, and are being generally used in China.

for physical skills are memories of just how to co-ordinate certain sensa-
tions of weight, balance and muscle tension with certain muscular
efforts and how to time them. Skills may also involve judgments of the
position or movement of other objects, also based to a large extent on
experience. Obviously, the whole of athletics as we know it would
become futile, if any physically fit individual could be given the skill of
the star performer overnight. The same would be true of musical performance, dancing and other artistic activities.

The interesting question, of course, is: who will be the donors? As
with transplantation, we might expect social pressure on well-informed
people to leave their brains to universities. Eventually, perhaps, it may be
possible to synthesize memories, perhaps by copying the memory-mole-
cules contained in a 'molecular library'. It will then be possible to make
up any particular combination of memories which may be required,
including even memories of things which never happened. The falsifica-
tion of history for political ends will then take on a new aspect. The
memory factories will become military targets of importance, and memory-
spying will give espionage a new preoccupation.

There is still one other somewhat curious prospect to consider. Since, in
some of Jacobson's experiments, memories acquired by hamsters were
reported to have been conveyed to rats, it might therefore be possible
for men to acquire the memories of animals. Perhaps the thrill-seekers
who nowadays take a 'trip' with LSD-25 or psilocybin may seek to
roam the jungle, in retrospect, like the king of beasts, or know what it
feels like to be a reptile or a tapeworm.

Meanwhile, what is being done to provide people like you and me
with a less fallible memory than the one we have?

For older people at least there is a hope. In the early sixties, a Canadian
doctor, Ewen Cameron, Director of the Allen Memorial Institute of
Psychiatry at McGill, tried the experiment of giving RNA to elderly
patients, suffering from senile memory defect, and detected some improvement, though deterioration resumed when the treatment stopped.
The difficulty of obtaining sufficient RNA of suitable purity restricted his
experiments, but he is confirming them in the U.S.A., in Albany.
Then, around 1965, an American drug company, Abbott Laboratories
of Chicago, announced the discovery of magnesium pemoline (trade
name: Cylert), which improved recovery from the amnesia caused by

electroshock. Dr Alvin Glasky tested many products to find it. Dr Cameron was quick to obtain the 'memory drug' for testing on human patients (not permitted at that time in the U.S.A.), and in 1966 reported his preliminary results. The drug was given by mouth to 24 patients with 'severe memory deficits due to senility or pre-senile psychosis' and precautions were taken against the possibility of suggestion. Placebos were employed on a double-blind basis: neither patients nor doctors knew, until after, which patient had had the drug and which the placebo.

For a week, there was no effect. Then the patients began to improve on memory tests. Relatives also reported improvement. 'My husband, who was an excellent bridge player and had to give it up, is now playing again,' said one wife. Another, who had forgotten how to switch on the television set, surely the ultimate disaster in our civilization, recovered this vital faculty. Experiments to see if Cylert will help those who have memory deficits due to carbon dioxide poisoning, overdoses of anaesthetics or automobile accidents, are to follow.

Of course, we do not yet know what causes the impaired memory of old age, and in some cases it is total and may be due to a failure of read-in, as distinct from the failure of read-out which is what bothers us in middle life. Yet it would seem reasonable to hope at least for some improvement of the defects of senility – whether the same treatment will have any effect on normal people has yet to be shown. Dr Cameron is optimistic.

'A century ago it was considered usual for men to be obese,' he says. 'And all mill girls had false teeth before they were forty years old. It was considered normal. . . . Now, with better dental care, it doesn't happen. So it *isn't* normal to have mental lapses.'

Memory, of course, is a factor in intelligence, as the word is generally used, for a person who knows nothing cannot behave intelligently. But to the psychologist, intelligence means something more specific – an ability to make use of data and to see the patterns it falls into. Most people admire intelligence, even if they distrust it; or perhaps it is intelligence divorced from feeling which they distrust. Certainly, most parents are concerned if their children rate low in IQ tests. The efforts which some researchers are making towards raising intelligence are therefore of more than academic importance.

Intelligence for all?

The great mathematician Karl Friedrich Gauss, probably one of the most acutely intelligent men who ever lived, was the son of a bricklayer. He showed signs of his superior intellectual powers from a very early age. Once, for instance, when at infant school, the teacher told the pupils to add up every number from one to a hundred. The other children started busily scratching away at their slates, but young Gauss put up his hand and announced the answer: 5050. He had immediately seen that 99 and 1 make a pair adding to 100; so do 98 and 2, 97 and 3 and so on. There are 49 such pairs, with a middle term of 50, making 4950. The addition of the final 100 brings the total to 5050. All done in the head, by a stroke of insight.

It would be a titanic thing for the human race if we were all a bit nearer Gauss in intelligence. What are the prospects? What was there about the grey matter within Gauss's head which differed from the grey matter in yours and mine? The answer to the latter question at least is becoming clear, and experiments are under way to exploit the knowledge.

Intelligence is only loosely connected with the size and weight of the brain-mass. While it is true that man has a bigger brain than an ape, and an ape than a cat, yet impressions taken from the skulls of eminent men show brain-masses well within the normal human range.* It seems almost certain that the prime factor in intelligence is the number and the nature of the interconnections between the hundred million cells in the brain.

The brain contains two types of cells: neurones which are believed to do the actual work, and glial cells which are believed to support them and supply them with energy. Glial cells may also conceivably be the repository of memory. They outnumber the neurones – indeed two-thirds of the brain's mass consists of neuroglia – and have been until recently neglected, being regarded simply as a matrix for the neurones. There may be some surprises in store when they are more fully investigated.

The neurones, unlike most other cells, do not increase in number by

* Experiments on animals in which part of the cerebral cortex, the outer part of the brain, is removed, show little loss of capacity to perform learned routines, until the amount removed is considerable. The brain seems to have a good deal of spare capacity.

division, so that the brain, once it is formed, cannot be developed in the way that muscles can, by actual growth. But each neurone puts out delicate processes which squirm about like living things and make contact with other neurones. If these contacts prove useful, they are consolidated, if not they are reabsorbed. Whether they are consolidated seems to depend upon whether, from time to time, an electric current passes along them – whether the circuit is proving to be needed. Thus every brain is 'wired' in a unique manner which reflects the life experience of its owner. The brain of a tennis player is wired differently from the brain of a philosopher but similarly, in some respects, to the brains of other tennis players. (This has not, of course, been demonstrated, owing partly to the difficulty of obtaining human brains of desired types, but mostly to the difficulty of tracing neuronal connections.)

Each neurone emits a tiny pulse of electricity when stimulated by the pulse arriving from a connecting neurone, provided the pulse is strong enough: its threshold of sensitivity to different neighbouring neurones varies, and is lowered with repeated use, raised if neglected. In this sense too, therefore, each brain is unique: the setting of the neuronal thresholds reflects the owner's life experience.

It follows, therefore, that there is no prospect of devising drugs or treatments which will instantly turn a mediocre adult brain into that of a Gauss, a Beethoven, a Shakespeare or even a brilliant athlete or tennis player. It is possible, however, that drugs may be developed which will bring about some lesser improvement of performance. Most of us do not make the best use of what we know, and there are times when we feel 'too tired to think'. Drugs like amphetamine dispel this tiredness, prolonging our thinking time and enabling us to marshal the facts we know, though they cannot tell us what we do not know.

It has been noticed, for instance, that the brains of rats which are cleverer at threading mazes contain more of the enzyme cholinesterase than the duller rats, and, as we come to see that brain function depends as much on chemistry as on electronics, some scientists have begun to visualize drugs which would improve brain function just as we intervene in nutrition with artificial vitamins. Thus Professor Jean Rostand writes: 'There is no prior reason why we should not succeed in stimulating the working of the brain, just as we do with other less exalted vital parts. . . . Even if the use of these future drugs resulted in no more than a few minutes of 'super thought' per day, and if these flashes were paid for by long periods of depression, mankind would still find it worth while to produce them. . . .'

The probability is that most of us do not use the capacity that we already have to anything like the limit. The great Italian educator and physician Mme Maria Montessori holds that children can do higher mathematics by the age of eight if they are encouraged to work to the limits of what they believe their own capacities to be.

We may therefore treat with some reserve a recent revolutionary suggestion for making use of the brain's spare capacity. The brain consists of two symmetrical halves. In right-handed people, it is the left half which does most of the work – it is said to be 'dominant'. The other half seems to be simply reserve capacity: there are numerous connections between the two halves and it has been shown, by separating the optic nerves so that each half-brain is connected to one eye only, that lessons learned by one half are soon written into the other also. This could explain why victims of 'stroke', with one half of their brain damaged, may gradually recover the use of their faculties: the unused half of the brain takes over.

Could we, then, exploit this reserve capacity? This is reported to be the aim of a group of neurologists, educators and other researchers who are busy organizing a group of Institutes for the Achievement of Human Potential. If they succeed, they might produce a new line of geniuses, equally at home in higher mathematics and in the kitchen garden. However, as Bertrand Russell has said, 'Men fear thought as they fear nothing else on earth – more than ruin, more even than death.' So they may not prove very popular.

While it seems unlikely that any drug or treatment will be found which will bestow on the adult human being a dramatically increased intelligence, the position is quite different for those who are still at the start of their programme of development. At this stage it is still possible to stimulate the development of the neuronal network. Thus Professor S. Zamenhof and his team at the University of California have tried injecting pregnant mice and rats with pituitary growth hormone, while the brain of the offspring was still maturing. They gave injections from the seventh to the twelfth day of pregnancy. Subsequently they killed the offspring and examined their brains closely. They found not only a significant increase in brain weight but also an increase in the ratio of neurones to the supporting glial cells. More important still, they discovered that the density of cells in the cortex, where reasoning is carried out, was increased and that the number and length of the dendrites – the branching interconnections – was greater. According to another group working on this idea, the chance of a neurone making contact with another brain cell is enhanced by an estimated fifty per cent in such animals. Similar brain enlargement was also found in parallel experiments on tadpoles, while other workers report that these hepped-up rats showed improved performance at standard maze-running tests.

While these results have been achieved with animals, a somewhat less drastic treatment has been applied to human babies in South Africa.

At the University of Witwatersrand, the Dean of the Medical Faculty, Professor O. S. Heyns, developed a technique of keeping pregnant women with their abdomen and pelvis inside a plastic enclosure, the pressure in which is reduced by a pump to one-fifth atmospheric pressure, a procedure he calls decompression, or foetal oxygenation. The treatment is given for half an hour daily, during the last ten days of pregnancy and during the beginning of labour. The reduction in pressure on the uterus was planned to reduce the pains of childbirth, and it also helps the maternal blood to circulate more freely.

Professor Heyns was surprised when, a year or so after his first experiments, he began to get reports from their mothers that the children born in these conditions were exceptionally intelligent, and certainly forward in their physical development. At first these reports were ignored on the grounds that all mothers believe their new baby to be exceptional. But soon it was found that some of these super-oxygenated babies really were exceptional – like Katl Oertel, who was answering the telephone at 13 months, and was speaking in four languages by the age of three. (These babies commonly hear four languages spoken around them – English, German, Zulu and Afrikaans – but normal babies speak the tongue their mother speaks to them.) These super-children were bored at their nursery schools; they chat with adults in a fluent, unconcerned sort of way which suggests a maturity which usually comes far later. A vocabulary of 200 words by age 18 months is common with them: the average child speaks only half a dozen words at this age.

Critics say, however, that it is impossible to measure intelligence in two-year-old children in any reliable way, and several more years must pass

before it can be proved that these children will make unusually intelligent adults. It is further objected that only the more intelligent mothers
offered themselves to try Professor Heyns' new method and, since intellectual capacity may have hereditary components, the sample may be
biased.

In the last weeks of pregnancy, the placenta does not grow any further,
and the infant's heart becomes incapable of driving blood through it. Professor Heyns believes that, in consequence, the brains of most foetuses
fail to develop to their full capacity since the foetus's oxygen demands
outstrip the capacity of the mother to supply it. The oxygenation of the
mother's blood helps to remedy this deficiency.

Whether these children continue to stay ahead is a matter to watch with
close attention. This could prove one of the most significant experiments
of our generation.

Apart from the rather macabre possibilities inherent in the work of
Professors Zamenhof and Heyns, there is a very real possibility of achieving a small but definite improvement of intelligence, taking the population
as a whole, by improving the environment in which the young child is
brought up.

The fact that the children of intelligent parents tend to be above average
in intelligence has long been noted; and it has been argued that this is not
hereditary, but due to the fact that they find themselves in a more intellectually stimulating environment. (Against this, however, it has been
shown that one-egg twins, separated at birth and brought up in widely
different environments, tend to achieve similar IQ ratings. Thus, in a
case where one twin was brought up in a university family at Oxford,
and the other on a Welsh farm, their IQs were only a couple of points
apart when measured. Brothers and sisters also show closer IQs, even when
brought up separately, than do adopted children brought up in the same
home. All of which argues a strong hereditary factor.) But that there is
some truth in the view that environment matters is suggested by the work
of Drs David Krech and Edward L. Bennett of Berkeley. They separated
rats twenty-five days after birth and placed some in solitary confinement,
the others in cages where there was plenty to do: ropes to climb, wheels to
turn, and so on. Later, the first group scored lower on 'intelligence' tests
than the latter. At fifteen weeks, they killed all the animals and dissected
their brains. They found that, in the privileged group, the cortex was

thicker and that the proportion of cortex to sub-cortex correlated with the speed at which they had learned to run mazes. The number of neurones was not increased, but their size and number of branchings seemed to be. There were certainly more glial cells, and more cholinesterase and acetyl-cholinesterase in them.

The British paper *Science Journal* commented: 'The most exciting implications of this research come from the strong probability that the results with rats can be extended to humans. This American work seems to be the first solid evidence from studies of the brain itself that intelligence can in fact be cultivated. This provides a wholly new line of support for the suggestions of some psychologists that the nature of the early environ-ment has a critical bearing on the development of effective intelligence in later life. . . .'

It also seems probable that undernourishment in early life permanently handicaps brain development.

It is safe to assume that a majority of the population in western coun-tries does not benefit from an optimal environment in childhood, in the sense here considered. By improving this situation, IQs could almost certainly be raised by ten or fifteen points in many individuals. If this seems a small gain, compared with the dramatic possibilities discussed earlier, it should be borne in mind that a shift of only 1·5 per cent in the IQ of the entire population would more than double the number of people with IQs over 160 – sometimes described as the genius level, though perhaps highly talented would be a more realistic descrip-tion.

In short, we can expect to see significant changes in global intelligence in those developing countries which are improving nutritional standards. Whether we shall see a decline in those western countries in which the quality of emotional relationships in the home is too often poor and else-where deteriorating raises issues so general that I shall leave them to another chapter.

Controlling pain

Before turning to wider issues, there is one further research area which demands our attention – the control of pain. Here, too, the rate of progress is accelerating.

It was in 1842 that Crawford W. Long of Jefferson, Georgia, per-formed the first operation under ether, the removal of a small tumour on the patient's neck. (Actually, this was not a 'first' in anaesthesia. The Greek doctor Dioscorides, who was surgeon-general of Nero's armies, knew of local and general anaesthesia, and even of rectal administration of narcotics, and was the first to use the word in its modern sense. The 'soporific sponge' is also mentioned from time to time in medieval writings.) But with Long's operation the modern era of chemical anaesthetics dawned, and in the century or so which has since elapsed, no radical changes have taken place. New and swifter anaesthetics have been found, with fewer side-effects, but until recently there has been nothing more than consolidation of the original advance.

Oddly enough, no one really understands why chemical anaesthetics produce their effect, or even where in the brain they act. Yet millions of people have reason to be grateful to those who fought down the prejudice which existed against the new chemical anaesthetics, and the idea that the best way to dull or banish pain is by chemical means has become taken for granted.

But nervous activity is electrical in nature, and at this very moment a new chapter in the control of pain is being opened – the use of electrical devices.

In 1965 two Harvard investigators exhibited a portable electronic device about the size of a transistor radio, capable of subduing even the intractable pain of cancer. The device is only for people with really severe pain, since it involves the insertion of electrodes into the brain through an opening drilled in the skull. The electrodes are placed in a structure known as the thalamus, and nine-volt thirty-cycles-per-second current can be administered by pressing a button. Pain is suppressed for many hours after about an hour's treatment, and there is no damage to brain tissue. The developers of this device are Dr Frank Ervin, a neuro-surgeon, and Dr Vernon Mark, a neurologist. One patient with cancer of the larynx, Dr Ervin reported, had required 100 mg. of a morphine analogue every two hours to relieve his pain. After using the 'pain box' he had gone for three months without having to take pain-relieving drugs. Dr Mark reported similar results. Patients carry the box in the pocket of their dressing gown or pyjamas and turn it on whenever pain occurs. They report no side-effects.

But pain can also be controlled electronically, in some cases, by devices which do not call for anything so drastic as surgical insertion of electrodes in the skull.

Dr Patrick Wall was struck by the fact that soldiers hit by a bullet often feel no pain for some hours, even though they may still feel the prick of the needle if blood is taken for analysis. Victims of motor and other accidents also display this self-induced anaesthesia. Dr Wall argued from this that the body must include 'gates' which can block or let through pain impulses. He believes these gates are located in a part of the spinal substance known as the substantia gelatinosa or gelatinous substance. Blocking occurs when specialized cells receive a large number of weak impulses – and this is why we scratch a wider area when we scratch an itch. The numerous weak impulses from the scratched area block the pain from the single nerve ending which constitutes the itching.

With Dr William H. Sweet of the Department of Neurosurgery at Massachusetts General Hospital, Dr Wall, who works in the Biology Department at MIT, attached electrodes to people suffering from pain in limbs or other superficial parts of the body, and fed them with brief pulses at 100 times a second. One of their patients was a man who had received a bullet wound through his shoulder. He reported an intense pain in his fingers, 'like a blowtorch being passed over them'. The electrical stimulation dispelled the pain, or as another patient, a pharmacist, put it: 'The buzzing masks the pain.' Success was also had in treating superficial cancers, though the use of surface electrodes did not act on pain in deep-lying organs. After some months, it is true, the effectiveness of the treatment began to decline, and research is continuing.

The control of pain is also being approached in a different way. In the last few years it has been found that patients likely to suffer pain can be made drowsy and insensitive to pain, without becoming completely unconscious, by giving them analgesics such as phentanyl in conjunction with butyrophenones, such as haloperidol. For purposes such as an operation for Parkinsonism, or the insertion of bronchoscopes through the throat to inspect the lungs, it is better to have a patient who is awake and co-operative. This new technique, known as ataralgesia (meaning: no disturbance of mind or feeling of pain) is therefore superior to anaesthesia in such cases. The patient remains relaxed with a normally pink complexion and no feeling of nausea – very different from the pale, sweating, retching patient usually seen in bronchoscopy or intubation. Where an alert patient is not a requirement, however, light anaethesia can be super-imposed on the ataralgesia.

As dentists know, the unpleasantness of pain varies a great deal with one's attitude to it – the tense, worried person feels more pain than the relaxed one, from the same stimulus. This is the main reason that taking alcohol reduces the feeling of pain. The same is true of tranquillizers. As one scientist put it: chlorpromazine removes the harrowing element in pain.

Pain, in point of fact, is a more complex mechanism than is usually supposed. Why is it that, in some conditions, the lightest brushing of the affected part soon produces intense pain? The answer appears to lie in the fact that injured tissue can release substances, not yet fully understood, which in some way sensitize nerves to pain. These include histamine and 5-hydroxy-tryptamine, known as 5-HT for short. Wasps and hornets inject both these substances with their venom, as do octopuses and nettles. This is why their trifling stings, far less than a bramble scratch in a mechanical sense, are so painful. It may be, too, that some tumours also produce these substances.

Professor C. A. Keele, of the Department of Pharmacology and Therapeutics at Middlesex Hospital Medical School, is hopeful that in the next five or ten years a new drug with antagonistic effects on these substances will be isolated. There is already a drug named nalorphine which does so, but it has unwanted side-effects.

As these three reports show, both from the electrical and the chemical angle man's power to control pain is becoming steadily more absolute. It is logical to assume, therefore, that before very long most, perhaps all, forms of pain will be in principle controllable, and control methods will become simpler and more reliable. Probably no one will be without his own portable pain-control unit, to be used in case of mischance. But, equally, this knowledge will give men increased power to inflict pain scientifically to any limit. Torturers will rely upon biochemists, and the latter may have to ask themselves whether to release their findings freely, and if so, how and to whom. When the technique of torture has thus become absolute, all expectation of captured personnel heroically remaining silent will become vain. International regulations will be desirable, but impossible to enforce. The prospect is not pleasant.

Mind control

'As we stand at the threshold of the chemopsychiatric era and look towards the future, some may feel disposed to cheer and some to shudder,' Dr Robert de Ropp has written. The shudder is caused, one assumes, by the fear that ability to modify the mind may lead to ability to control the mind. Is this a legitimate extrapolation? Does the ability to relieve the suicidal depression of a psychotic, or to calm the anxieties of a neurotic, really imply ability to impose moods and attitudes on people, at variance with their real nature?

The question is not an easy one, and raises, among other things, the question of what *is* one's real nature. If a man grows querulous and embittered with age, is this his 'real nature'? Do we have a basic personality on which life imposes distortions, or is our personality entirely the construct of our experience? In so far as the question originally raised reflects a fear that our personal uniqueness and individuality is at risk, these are relevant questions. If, on the other hand, we are simply concerned with how far political misuse could be made of our new powers, the matter becomes much simpler.

The drugs available at present are limited in scope. They consist, as we have seen, of ataractics (or tranquillizers), analeptics (or stimulants) and psychotomimetics. Drugs of this kind might be misused – for instance they might be given surreptitiously to prisoners of war, to reduce the likelihood of their attempting an escape. (True, anaesthetics can also be misused, for example by housebreakers or kidnappers, but at least it is clear to all when and if they have been used.)

It is hardly to be visualized, however, that they could be used surreptitiously to ensure support of a political programme, say, though conceivably a dictator could openly add them to the diet or distribute them like vitamin pills. Perhaps it is not out of the question that drugs might be found which greatly increased suggestibility, which could be convenient to a dictator controlling propaganda media.

Some years ago, there was a considerable stir when experiments were conducted in subliminal stimulation. Words were flashed on a cinema screen, in the course of running a film of general interest, so briefly that they were not consciously seen. Yet they could be shown to have regis-tered on the brain by associative tests given afterwards. Advertisers at once thought this an interesting technique for stimulating the sale of their goods. If a word – such as a brand-name – could be presented sublimin-ally, during television or cinema programmes, would not the viewers be more likely to ask for this product? In Britain, the U.S.A. and elsewhere, such techniques were soon banned or voluntarily renounced. It is not clear, however, whether they would have been effective. In one experi-mental run, before the ban, the word 'ice-cream' was subliminally presented to a cinema audience, in the expectation that the sale of ice-cream during the interval would increase. It did increase slightly, but other patrons complained to the management that the theatre was too cold, though it was in fact at the same temperature as usual. The outcome of such stimulation in action is therefore somewhat unpredictable, in the present state of the art.

There are also other directions in which behaviour might be in-fluenced. For instance, Dr R. P. Michael at the Institute of Psychiatry in London gave oestrogens to female rhesus monkeys and found that this evoked sexual excitement in near-by males. Apparently it stimulated the females to produce a sex-attractant, probably olfactory in nature. Such processes have been thoroughly studied in insects and were thought to be peculiar to them. Quite recently it has been realized they occur in mam-mals also. It is therefore highly probable that they also occur in man, and Dr H. Wiener of New York claims that they do, calling these chemical messengers ECM's. He believes that they can signal anger, hate and fear as well as desire.

Throughout the ages, of course, women have employed perfumes as sexual stimulants to the male, not wholly without effect. Such activity is related to the controlled chemistry of which I am speaking in much the same way that a witch's use of foxgloves for dropsy is related to the medical use of digitalis today. We can reasonably expect that while perfumes sometimes unreliably perform what is expected of them, the synthesized attractants of the future will work wholly reliably and with precision.

(Incidentally, since oestrogens are the main component of contraceptive pills, it could be interesting to see whether their use by a woman affects her husband's desire.)

The British journal New Scientist saw in this development 'a possible clue to the little-understood factors regulating group and mass behaviour', and wondered whether dictators of the future might not 'maintain control by the use of appropriately formulated aerosols, piped from a central behaviour-plant to every factory, office and home'. The answer must surely be: only in the dictatorial world of Orwell's *1984*. In any other world the solution would be to put a sock in it.

More interesting perhaps is the reverse possibility: that one might be able to switch desire off, and embrace chastity without a further effort of will – such a course might be convenient, at least, for explorers, astro-nauts and others cut off from the society of the opposite sex. In prisons where abnormal sexual behaviour commonly occurs, as a result of such isolation, the use of such an anaphrodisiac might be justifiable, parallel-ing the alleged use of flowers of sulphur in the past for the same purpose.

Again, the hormone prolactin stimulates maternal behaviour in animals, and if injected into males, causes them to perform the appro-priate maternal behaviour of their species. Humans are less under the sway of instinct, perhaps, and it would be interesting to see whether un-satisfactory mothers could be made more motherly by injections of such a drug; or indeed to discover whether their 'unnatural' behaviour was due to some constitutional lack of it – in which case its use would be fully justified as a form of 'replacement therapy'.

One form of mental control which has already become the subject of debate is the attempt to secure that a witness speaks the truth. The so-called 'lie detector' (which actually measures anxiety as reflected by changes in skin resistance, breathing or heart-rate) has been in use in some states of the U.S.A. for periods up to thirty years. The results are notori-ously unreliable, since a man may have other reasons for anxiety than guilt, while some guilty men are preternaturally free from concern about their crime.

It is an interesting point that the subjects of such enquiries can also resort to scientific methods to resist the inquisition. Thus in December 1957, residents in Newbury, Vermont, were given lie-detector tests in connection with the violent death of a local farmer. He had been highly unpopular, and some people thought he had been put to death by neighbours in a 'white lynching'. The persons interrogated with the 'lie detector' all took the precaution of taking the tranquillizer meprobamate before undergoing the test: one effect of this drug is to raise the response level of the skin. As a result the tests were of no value.

Where authority is in a position to expose an individual to prolonged stresses, as in the case of 'brain-washing', the withholding of information may become difficult, and there can be little doubt that these methods will be developed to the point where silence becomes impossible – if this is not already the case. This is not the place to go into the complex psychology of current techniques, but it may be well to justify the foregoing assertion by reference to a more physiological approach, currently being explored. There are centres in the brain which control eating, drinking, sleeping and perhaps other activities. If the appropriate centre is stimulated, an animal which is already sated with food will eat more, a waterlogged animal will drink. Some human patients with tumours or other disturbances of these regions are known: such people may eat to excess, for instance, or refuse food when starving. No one can resist these compulsions; equally when sexual needs are thus stimulated they become overwhelming. Other centres have an even more crucial role, and rats will ignore food and sex when they are stimulated, to the point of starvation. At present such stimulation can only be achieved by surgical intervention: electrodes must be inserted in the brain or chemicals dripped into it through a tube. But what if they could be stimulated by drugs or other methods which leave no visible scar? Would a soldier, the very mechanisms of whose brain had been tampered with, be able to resist the demand to supply information? It is most unlikely. Professor James G. Miller, the director of the Mental Health Research Institute of Ann Arbor, Michigan, has commented: 'Our present code of conduct for the military forces is not prepared for technical developments in brain-washing, any more than is the general concept of the average citizen.' To order a man to resist brain-washing, he adds, may be like ordering a man under anaesthesia to stand at attention.

Dr Jonathan O. Cole, the Chief of the Psychopharmacology Service Center of the National Institutes of Health, takes an optimistic view: he maintains that we are not in a position to engineer drugs with the effect we want, since most of the known drugs have widely varying effects on different patients. He concludes:

I consider it unlikely that current methods can be used to develop a new drug with any specific and reliable effect on either the freedom or the control of human mental processes, although I confidently expect that new types of drugs with different effects on brain functioning and behaviour will be uncovered by present drugs development methods. . . . The difficulties appear to be well-nigh insurmountable.

But Professor B. F. Skinner takes a different view. Arguing that behaviour can be, or is about to be, controlled effectively, he concludes that it is 'the duty of our society to attempt actively to control human behaviour in such a way as to achieve the effects we consider desirable before some other group becomes more proficient at controlling behaviour and directing it into paths we consider undesirable.'

All depends on what we do with this new knowledge. Professor Miller warns us that 'drug research could lead to a new tyranny beyond Jefferson's imagination . . . to control of man's acts by chemical strings. But it need not make him a puppet . . . it may increase the number of his alternatives of choice and so his individuality and freedom.'

There is also substance, I believe, in the fear that a hypertrophy of the memory and intelligence might lead to an 'inhuman' sort of society. By 'human' we tend to mean like ourselves and other human beings we know – and most of these will be of average intelligence, given to errors and misjudgments, often letting their emotions overrule their judgment, and so on. The kind of people which these developments may create will evidently be different from us, and we might find ourselves ill at ease with them. But then, the cruel and murderous knights of the thirteenth century would be extremely ill at ease in a modern drawing room or golf club. There is no reason to suppose that the intelligent denizens of future society will feel their world to be inhuman – since, for them, 'human' will mean like themselves.

But we can press the point a little further. The average man tends to distrust intelligence: he feels that high intelligence means low emotional involvement, and that where emotions are left out the reasoning power tends to arrive at decisions which, though logical, are not always acceptable. It is not an answer to say that a very intelligent person will allow for the emotional factors, since to allow for something and to feel it are by no means the same thing. It is possible, at this point, to proceed to split a good many philosophical hairs, but I think that the central point cannot be argued away; man needs to maintain a due balance between thinking and feeling, and often fails to do so. Unless, therefore, an appropriate amount of effort is put into the probably more difficult task of producing emotionally mature, responsive and balanced individuals, any recipe for the rapid improvement of intelligence might prove to have objectionable effects, even disastrous ones.

Besides this fundamental issue, there is in the shorter term the danger of creating an élite group, all the more dangerous socially because it will be genuinely an élite. Those who have been operated on at birth, or subjected to the oxygenating treatment, may well feel a genuine kinship with other super-brains, and as a group the super-brains may tend to work for their own preferential treatment, even if they do not actually seek to take over the reins of power. Even more in line with science-fiction thinking – and science-fiction writers tend to take a darkly pessimistic view of the future – is the possibility that such an élite, having assumed power, should deny the treatment which produces intelligence to any but a minority, perhaps their own offspring, thus perpetuating a two-caste society. By permitting varying degrees of treatment, a society with three, four or more intellectual castes could readily be produced.

Even if we do not push the prediction to these extremes, we can see that the possibility of a have and a have-not group, intellectually speaking, in society is a real one. Moreover, if the industrialized nations are the first to adopt such methods, there might be a widened gap between the developing and the developed countries, the latter tending to advance even more rapidly owing to their enhanced brain power.

The French statesman of science Pierre Auger has asked whether there are some operations beyond the capacity of the human brain as we know it. It may equally be asked whether an enlarged brain might not carry man above some threshold as yet uncrossed. When the brain became large enough and complex enough to compass speech, man diverged from the animals. Men with still better brains might have capacities which we cannot even envisage and as such would constitute a different species, even a different order of beings from ourselves.

Looking at brain research as a whole, I find it difficult to avoid the impression that it will create more serious social problems than any other area of biological enquiry. Professor Donald MacKay, of Keele University, who has written many papers and articles on the philosophical and religious aspects of what we know about the brain, declared recently in *Science Journal*: 'The possibilities of misapplication of the results of brain science are already frightening to many people. Could it be, they ask, that here at last we face the ultimate Pandora's Box, a secret whose uncovering would be the destruction of human society? Has brain research gone far enough, if not too far, already?'

To these questions he returns a negative answer on the shaky grounds that scientists have a duty to study everything and that one can never tell how anything will turn out. Personally, I think both these statements to be true, but that by no means convinces me that the future is not likely to be disastrous. Actually the premises and the conclusions are not logically connected and the remark may strike many people as typical of the woolly optimism to which so many scientists are given.

6

The Genetic Engineers

To judge from what scientists themselves are saying, the most serious of all the human problems created by biological research is constituted by man's imminent power to interfere in the processes of heredity, to alter the genetic structure of his own species.

The desirability of improving the human stock has long been recognized, and the fear that it could deteriorate in the absence of such a policy is equally ancient. Thus Plato proposed an eugenic programme, putting into the mouth of Socrates the words: 'In the same way, if we want to prevent the human race from degenerating, we shall take care to encourage union between the better specimens of both sexes, and to limit that of the worse.' In the ideal city proposed by Campanella at the beginning of the seventeenth century there was even a Ministry of Love. Hitler actually attempted to put a limited eugenic programme into practice, establishing Ordensburgen where selected young SS men of 'Aryan' appearance were to live and encouraging 'Aryan' maidens to undertake to bear children by them in the interests of the Fatherland.

Man has long had the power to attempt to improve the stock by the methods of the plant and animal breeder, but it has proved difficult to persuade people to mate for eugenic reasons. New techniques such as those described in Chapter 2 could simplify matters. The procedure of sexual enjoyment has finally become wholly divorceable from the procedure of procreation. Contraception can be used to prevent procreation when the sexual act is performed, while artificial insemination and artificial inovulation, separately or together, can be used to bring about procreation without the occurrence of the sexual act. Thus it becomes possible to introduce an eugenic policy without interfering in people's choice of mate or a marital partner.

No one knows how far people would respond to an appeal to have their babies by such methods. Most parents have an understandable desire to produce children which are truly theirs, and experience with adopted children gives some colour to the idea that children who differ genetically from their parents may be harder to bring up and may feel themselves in an alien environment, though it is hard to know at present how far this is due to the adopted child's loss of its biological parents. On the other hand, if, in a country like Russia or China, a massive appeal were made by the state to support an eugenic policy based on AID, on patriotic grounds, it is not too improbable that large numbers of people would respond. No one knows what would be the effect on family life if they did.

In any case, it is estimated that 10,000 artificially inseminated concep-tions occur in the United States every year, and the number is rising. At present there is little systematic control and certainly no attempt to ensure that these conceptions, at least, shall be above average genetically. Except that donors with obvious genetic defects are excluded, no scien-tific selection is made and the offspring are just as likely to be below stand-ard as above it.

If only for this reason, it would be worth devoting some attention to the practicability of eugenic policies. But what has inspired the current sense of excitement among biologists is something much more drastic: the prospect of being able to insert, deliberately, specific factors (genes) into the genetic material. As if one should be able to say, for instance: 'I wish my son to be exactly like me, except that he should have better teeth and red hair.'

Terms such as 'gene surgery', 'gene copying', 'gene insertion' and 'gene deletion' are beginning to appear in scientific statements. References to 'algeny' or 'genetic engineering' are becoming common. Dr Edward L. Tatum of the Rockefeller Institute, a Nobel prizeman, has declared that 'we can foresee . . . purposeful manipulation of genetic change even in man', adding that biological engineering will come 'perhaps sooner than we anticipate'. And he has described this as 'the most astounding pros-pect so far suggested by science'.

Professor Bentley Glass, who is a Doctor of Laws as well as a biologist working in the field of human genetics, has warned us that though this may be feasible he is not prepared to say that it is advisable or wise, and tells us that 'within just a few years we must decide whether to permit such reproductive human engineering'.

The breakthrough – and for once the word is not an over-statement – which has occurred in the understanding of genetics represents one of the most dramatic success stories in biology, and before attempting to discuss its implications in detail, it will be worth summarizing the discoveries which have led up to the current sense of imminent crisis.

The DNA story

When men first began to think about the mechanism of inheritance, they thought, perhaps naturally, in terms of a mixture. But a German dog-breeder realized that when you cross two breeds, say a police dog and a Schnauzer, you often get offspring which seem to be one or the other and not a cross between the two. And plant breeders noticed that when you breed green, smooth-skinned peas with yellow, wrinkled ones, you may get peas which are green and smooth, green and wrinkled, yellow and smooth, or yellow and wrinkled. In other words, the tendency to be green is either inherited or not inherited, and quite independently of the tendency to be wrinkled or not wrinkled. But it was not for another quarter-century that the Moravian monk, Gregor Mendel, drew the explicit conclusion that inheritance occurs by the bringing together of what he called 'primal characters' from each parent, one of which sometimes dominates or obscures the other. (Thus, if a person inherits a factor for blue eyes from one parent, and a factor for brown eyes from the other, he will have brown eyes, but may still transmit a factor for blue eyes to his own offspring.) Living things, said Mendel, are a mosaic of independent hereditary factors.

It is these independent hereditary factors which we nowadays call genes.

While Mendel was working in obscurity, biologists were investigating the cells of which all living things are made, and with the improved oil-immersion microscope discovered within the nucleus of every cell dark rods, which split longitudinally when the cell divided, bestowing a similar assortment on each daughter cell. When, however, egg and sperm were being formed, the mechanism was different: only half the rods went into the daughter cell, be it sperm or egg, so that when, at fertilization, egg and sperm fused, the original number was restored. These rods were the chromosomes, and this was clearly the mechanism by which characters were reshuffled in passing from parent to child. This explained, too, why whole blocks of characters tended to be inherited together.

This inspired intensive studies of chromosomal inheritance, chiefly using the fruit fly, *Drosophila* – a convenient creature, since it requires little laboratory space, is hardy, and breeds in twelve days. Sometimes, it was noted, chromosomes would break and the parts would rejoin in a different pattern. By studying the hereditary changes which accompanied this, it was possible to work out where on each chromosome the genes for various characters lay. The work was laborious and was only developed in detail with *Drosophila*, which became the cornerstone of genetics.

But of what did the chromosomes consist, and how was the hereditary message carried? The next step was not taken until 1944, when Oswald Avery, an American immunochemist, performed one of the seminal experiments in the history of biology. By it he showed that the hereditary instructions are carried in the structure of the molecule of what was then an obscure acid, known as deoxyribose nucleic acid, or DNA for short. He took two strains of pneumococci, the bacteria which cause pneumonia, one of which had a rough coat or capsule, the other a smooth one. He extracted from the smooth one a substance in which he placed the rough-coated bacteria and allowed them to divide. He then found that some of them had acquired smooth coats and now transmitted this characteristic to their offspring when they in turn divided. He then purified the substance and showed that it was DNA. Thus DNA was indisputably the repository of hereditary information! Avery, actually, was spurred to make this experiment by the observations of an English bacteriologist, Fred Griffith, who, twelve years before, had inadvertently conveyed the virulence from one strain of pneumococci to another – a result which everyone declared at the time to be impossible, obviously due to a technical slip-up.

In another ten years, DNA had been shown to be a double molecule: two long molecular chains twisted together. Each of these chains is composed of units known as nucleotides, of which there are four kinds: it resembles a necklace made with four kinds of bead. The 'beads' are conveniently labelled A, C, G and T from the initial letters of the four types of chemical grouping composing them. Now, it happens to be the case that A will bind to G, if the two are brought together, and C to T. This serves to hold the two threads together, the bead pattern on one being complementary to the bead pattern on the other. Thus DNA is beautifully designed to pass on information. For, if the two chains are separated, and placed in a pool of nucleotides, the A's will pick up G's and so on, until there are two double molecules where there was one before. Each has specified how to build its counterpart.

In the whole of nature no other molecule with this extraordinary double-helix structure has ever been discovered – though it should be added that there is a single-stranded helical molecule, known as RNA, which can be formed on parts of the DNA chain and which, on being detached, conveys instructions to the working machinery of the cell, much as a wax-impression conveys information about the shape of a key. RNA thus constitutes a kind of carbon copy – or, better, a working drawing of how to make a particular protein, derived from the master blueprint. (A double-stranded RNA occurs in some viruses.)

The precise sequence of nucleotides in the DNA of any individual is unique, except in the case of identical twins (triplets, etc.). The molecule is enormously long: human DNA contains a thousand million nucleotides. Nevertheless, the DNA of all living creatures, both plant and animal, appears to be built on the same general plan.

The question may now be asked: how can something like a bead necklace regulate the formation and functioning of a cell?

A cell is a box with permeable walls which selectively admits a wide range of substances, which then take part in chemical reactions, producing substances required by the cell and waste products which are passed out again. The control of these chemical reactions is carried out by substances known as enzymes. There are thousands of kinds of enzymes and each one makes possible, by its presence, a particular chemical reaction. (Yeast is a well-known enzyme: it makes fermentation occur.) DNA works by producing, at the right moment, the right enzyme; and, in fact, it is broadly true that each gene evokes one specific enzyme.

This singular ability of enzymes seems to depend on their shapes, and different shapes fit different enzymes for different tasks, just as a hammer and a saw perform different tasks because of their shapes, despite the fact that both are made from wood and metal. The cell is thus a factory full of specialized tools and jigs. A typical mode of action seems to be for an enzyme molecule to attach itself to another molecule – say an amino acid – and in so doing to distort it slightly, so that it will now in turn fit itself to another amino acid. This distorts it further and releases the enzyme molecule to repeat the process. In this way, a single enzyme molecule can form a chain of amino acids. Other enzymes break up large molecules by a converse process.

Enzymes are members of the class of substances known as proteins, and these are defined as strings of the chemical building bricks known as amino acids, of which there are some twenty types. A typical protein may consist of some hundreds or thousands of amino acids, linked together in a precise sequence. The chain thus formed automatically balls itself up in a complicated way, because certain amino-acid combinations have a natural tendency to produce a change of direction in the chain. This is how every protein comes to have a distinctive shape, on which its biological properties depend. Proteins include a wide range of substances, from muscle to hormones, as well as enzymes. Obviously, in a chain of thousands of links, composed of twenty types of unit, an almost infinite variety of differently shaped proteins is possible. Thus, by a basically very simple device, nature provides an immensely varied range of biological materials.

We now come to the final stage of this involved story. It remains to explain how DNA evokes the required enzymes. It took another ten years' work to show that three nucleotides serve to specify one amino acid. Thus the combination ACG on the nucleic acid chain causes the amino acid lysine to be added to the protein chain which is being formed. The sequence of nucleotides required to specify a complete enzyme constitutes a gene, and since an enzyme contains a hundred or more amino acids, a sizeable piece of DNA is needed to do the job. It takes about 1000 genes to specify the enzymes for one cell and perhaps 100,000 to specify all the kinds of cell which make up a human being.

The DNA chain also appears to contain triplet-groups which serve as start and stop indications, so that the 'code' shall be read in the right manner.

A sequence of a dozen or more enzymes, controlling a sequence of reactions, may be required to produce a desired result – let us say the manufacture of a pigment which determines eye-colour. There seem to be switching genes which open up the whole section of DNA required to organize a specified result of this kind, and which close it off, or repress it, when enough of the required substance has been made. At any given moment, most of the genes in any one cell will be covered up or 're-pressed': if they were not, the cell would try to perform every possible reaction simultaneously. In a cell which has become specialized for a particular purpose, some may have become repressed indefinitely – but Professor Steward's work shows that they can, when needed, be released again. The mechanisms whereby, when a particular enzyme is needed, the appropriate gene is 'de-repressed' and proceeds to initiate manufacture of the required enzyme, are beginning to be understood, but we need not go into them here.

While a gene or group of genes may specify the formation of a pigment, the presence of which we can perceive with the naked eye in the organism which is eventually formed, the relationship between gene and visible character is generally less clear-cut. Many genes may interact to produce a given result; Professor C. H. Waddington of Edinburgh has compared the situation with a vast sheet of canvas tugged into complex curves by numerous guy-ropes, each rope symbolizing a gene.

The point is important, for it means that if a given gene is abolished it may simply produce a slight change in *several* visible features of the organism. So we cannot expect to eliminate some undesired character-istics simply by deleting one or two genes. It may take several, and these deletions may also adversely affect some characteristic we desire to retain, or even to improve. It is, to put it crudely, as if we could only improve intelligence at the cost of doing away with vision.

At present, of course, we have no idea, except in some very simple organisms – and then only a rough one – what is linked with what and how. Biologists believe that, by a long series of experiments in which different substitutions are made, the nature of these connections can be worked out. It may well be that it will be unnecessary to perform every possible experimental variation: there is probably a rationale which can be deduced, once a number of the elements in it are known. When that day comes, and it will certainly call for large computers to resolve so complex a pattern, it may conceivably be possible to write programmes for the construction of organisms, as we now write programmes with which automatic machine-tools proceed to make some required part. And from knowing the programmes (that is, nucleotide orders) which go to make known organisms, we could then go on to specify for combinations of characteristics which have never previously existed in nature, and indeed we could, with the aid of artificial gestation, go on to manufacture com' pletely novel organisms. Such methods would first be used, no doubt, for very simple organisms, such as bacteria; then to make improved plants and animals for agricultural purposes; but might finally be used to specify improved men or even superhuman creatures, far beyond men, for which we have at present no name.

To construct DNA's embodying such programmes should not prove impossibly difficult, as we shall see in a moment. The problem which may prove more awkward is to get the DNA thus fabricated into the germ cell where it can begin to do its work. But even this is not out of the question. Avery achieved it in bacteria, simple one-celled organisms, simply by soaking them in a DNA solution. Can anything similar be achieved with complex organisms, and above all, mammals?

Since the 1920's we have had, to be sure, crude methods of modifying the hereditary message. By blasting it with X-rays or with chemical substances known as mutagens, which damage the DNA, we can produce changes, most of them undesirable and many of them lethal. (Hence, of course, the objection to the radiation released by atomic bombs.)

Such deliberate induction of mutation is now being routinely employed in the interests of agriculture. Radiation, commonly from a radioactive cobalt source, is used to irradiate the specimen, causing a wide spectrum of mutations, most of which are undesirable and have to be scrapped, but one or two of which may constitute improvements. Thus in India it was desired to persuade the peasant farmers to change over from their traditional wheat to a rust-free variety with higher yields. But the tradi' tional wheat had a 'beard' on each grain which, the farmers claimed, discouraged birds from eating it. Though there was no scientific evidence for this, they could not be persuaded to plant the beardless rust-free wheat. Scientists at the Atomic Energy Research Station therefore irradiated the rustless wheat until eventually a bearded version appeared, and this the peasants are willing to accept.

In the case of men, of course, one cannot afford to throw away the unsuccessful variants. And methods of identifying specific defects, such as those already discussed, cannot be applied to the kind of general characteristics, such as intelligence or even disease-resistance, which manifest only in the adult organism: but it is precisely these which most interest us in the human case.

But there are now other intriguing possibilities.

Tinkering with heredity

In 1959, biologists heard a startling, even incredible, report from three French workers in Strasburg. They had taken, they said, two species of duck, Khaki Campbells and White Pekins. They had extracted DNA from the cells of the Khaki Campbells and had injected it into the White Pekins, thinking that just possibly the *offspring* of the latter might show some character derived from Khaki Campbells.

To their astonishment, the actual ducks they injected began to change. Their white feathers darkened and their necks began to take on the peculiar curve which is a mark of the Khaki Campbell. Other geneticists were incredulous but not so incredulous as not to attempt to repeat the experiments. Such attempts, which were made on rabbits, and other animals as well as ducks, failed, and the French workers were also unable to repeat the result. What actually happened remains a mystery.

But seven years later a genuine transformation, claimed as the first ever to be achieved except in bacteria, was announced by A. S. Fox and S. B. Yoon of Wisconsin University. They treated a strain of fruit flies – the geneticist's stock laboratory animal – with DNA extracted from flies of a different strain. The offspring of some of these flies varied genetically from their parents, and the variation bred true for up to seven generations, after which it vanished again. This announcement drew a reply from Professor Serge Gershenson, head of the Virology section of the Zabolotny Institute of Microbiology and Virology of the Academy of Sciences in the Ukraine. He, it appeared, had treated *Drosophila* with DNA derived from the thymus glands of calves thirty years ago, and had published his results in 1939. (At that time all DNA was believed to be identical, and he used calf DNA merely because there was a convenient technique available for obtaining it.) He found that the treatment produced stable mutations, but, unlike those produced by X-rays and so forth, these were not spread across the whole spectrum of possibilities, but confined chiefly to the structure of the wing, and indeed the treatment seemed to affect only one small segment of one chromosome.

At that time no explanation could be devised, and soon the war brought his work to a halt. Today, an explanation is easier to conceive. Presumably segments of injected DNA align themselves with segments of host DNA to which they are basically similar, and tend to go into action when the conditions which de-repress genes of that type are present. Of course, cows do not have wings, and it is to be assumed that there are short stretches of calf DNA which just happen to have much the same sequence as the fruit-fly-wing DNA. Or again, it may be that the triplet grouping of the injected DNA is changed in the process, so that the message is read from a different starting point, and thus is completely changed for another.

Moreover, we now know that viruses do their work by entering cells and substituting their own nucleic acid for the cell's nucleic acid, thus forcing the cell machinery to make viruses and not what the cell usually makes. And in the fifties it became clear that viruses can even pick up bits of nucleic acid from the cell they enter, adopt it into their own system and later deposit this 'rogue DNA' in another host cell – a phenomenon known as transduction.

This work leaves the field wide open for exciting advances. The presumption is that if DNA is taken from a wide variety of different sources, it will prove to induce various kinds of mutation when injected into different species. And though, in the west, only the lowly fruit fly has definitely been shown to accept foreign DNA directly, Professor Gershenson claims to have achieved transduction in a silkworm, using a virus to introduce the foreign DNA.* The next few years are thus sure to see a spate of experiments designed to test these findings and expand the range of possibilities. If the work is sound, as Professor Gershenson says, 'new perspectives will be opened up for the control of the mutation process.'

However, many workers believe that some less clumsy method of introducing DNA into a germ-cell is called for than simply soaking the egg in a solution of the nucleic acid. And it seems that one such way has already been found by Dr Teh Ping Lin of San Francisco. In 1966 he announced that he had succeeded in injecting fertilized mouse eggs with

* Since these lines were written drug resistance has been transferred from one mouse-cell line to another by DNA.

167

tiny quantities of bovine globulin without impairing their development.

Though micro-injection of non-mammalian eggs had been achieved before, no one had succeeded with mammalian eggs, which have a tough outer membrane. Furthermore, mammalian eggs are very small: a mouse egg is invisible to the naked eye – in fact it is only ten times the diameter of a human blood cell. Dr Teh managed to hold the eggs by sucking them into a micropipette with an internal diameter of fifteen thousandths of a millimetre, and then injected them with a micropipette only one thousandth of a millimetre in diameter. All this had to be done under the microscope, of course, with the aid of micromanipulators.

The eggs were then implanted in albino mice which had already been mated, so as to provide the correct hormonal environment, and allowed to develop. When the resulting baby mice were born the mother's own offspring could be identified by their pink eyes, and so distinguished from the implanted ones. About fifteen per cent of the injected eggs, it turned out, developed perfectly normally.

Dr Teh chose globulin as being a harmless substance, of natural origin, unlikely to cause damage; he was concerned only to show that the injection technique did not cause serious damage. But obviously the technique, once established, will be used to introduce many other agents, in order to explore their influence on development and thus help unravel the problems of embryology. Such agents will no doubt include hor-mones, and substances known to have a specific effect on development, such as thalidomide, and they will undoubtedly include DNA.

A year previously, however, Professor Henry Harris of the Sir William Dunn School of Pathology at Oxford University had announced yet another technique which will certainly contribute to the study of embry-onic development as well as having an impact on genetics.

Professor Harris's idea was to cause cells of widely different kinds to fuse and so to pool their genetic contents and cell machinery. He has used cells from different animals, such as mouse and rabbit, as well as cells from different tissues in the same animal. Such fusion of cells is known to occur occasionally in the plant world, notably in certain fungi, but the chance of it occurring in animals seemed, as Professor Harris puts it, 'rather remote', since animal cells contain such elaborate mechanisms for the recognition and rejection of foreign material.

The method by which he in fact achieved such fusion (thus showing, incidentally, that the recognition system must lie on the surface of cells and not within them) was to introduce a special virus. Known as Sendai, from its being first observed in the Sendai region of Malaya, it normally causes an influenzal type of infection, but it was found that it also caused certain cancer cells to fuse. Professor Harris showed that it had a similar effect on normal cells. He did not use live virus, which would naturally have complicated interpretation of the results, but virus which had been inactivated ('killed') with ultra-violet light.

The mere fact that such hybrid cells continue to function is confirm-atory evidence that DNA is built on the same plan throughout nature, and Harris comments: 'Perhaps none of the information which will flow from the study of these cells will be quite as exciting as the initial discovery that such cells could be produced at all.'

This is almost certainly unduly modest. By taking cells from different parts of the body, whose functions have become specialized, it should become possible to learn a great deal about how the information locked up in the DNA is released only when and where it is needed. Embryo-logists are beginning to exploit this technique, but so far there are no reports of the alternative application, the modification of the genetic message by bringing in other genetic material, and in particular by the application of this method to egg-cells. But the importance of its possible application to genetic engineering is obvious enough. The very fact that cells are tough enough to stand such treatment, and still function, and that they have no inherent objection to foreign nucleic acids is a cause for greatly increased confidence in the whole endeavour.

Genetic surgery

Whether current techniques will lead first to methods of deleting un-wanted genes, to methods of supplying missing genes, or whether the stage where whole blocks of characters can be altered simultaneously will be reached first, cannot yet be foreseen. Professor Edward Tatum has termed these possibilities gene deletion, gene insertion and gene surgery.

The microsurgery of DNA may possibly be achieved by physical methods: fine beams of radiation (probably laser light or pulsed X-rays) may be used to slice through the DNA molecule at desired points, or to knock out small sections, so as to eliminate specific defects. Alternatively, 'repressor molecules' may be found which can be introduced to block the expression of particular characteristics in a precise manner. It is already clear that certain molecules are so shaped that they can embed themselves between the projections on the DNA chain and it may be that this is how repressor molecules work.

Some scientists place more hope in the idea of using viruses to carry information into the cell. But it may be that the copying of desired DNA's or even the synthesis of DNA to a desired pattern will eliminate the need for such detailed tinkering. It will be enough to insert the required DNA molecule as a whole, perhaps by some development of Dr Teh's technique. Already molecules of the nucleic acid type, capable of assembling amino acids into protein-like structures, have been constructed in the laboratory. At present the message cannot be controlled in any real sense. The molecular biologist is like a telegraphist who cannot yet send messages: he can only send one letter repeatedly – AAAAAA or GGGGGG – or send random sequences such as AGCTCTAG. The step to being able to send actual 'words' cannot be far off: it could be taken tomorrow.

Thus Professor Tatum, at a gathering in 1966, spoke of tailoring genes by obtaining the desired genetic material and using enzymes to copy it, in unlimited quantities. He also envisaged the use of suppressor substances to delete unwanted genes, and touched on the development of 'gene insertion' – using nuclear grafts from healthy cells. Though there would be minor technical differences in treating germinal cells in this way, such experiments, he disclosed, were already being conducted in mammalian cells.

As the *New Scientist* commented at the time: he thus hinted 'at the culture of embryos in the laboratory, destined to develop into adults whose physical, and possibly intellectual, characteristics have been chosen in advance by the genetic engineers'.

One startling variation on this theme must be mentioned before we can discuss the wider implications of these developments. There seems to be no basic reason why one should not take the DNA from an egg and use it to fertilize another egg, whether by inserting it first into a spermatozoon or whether by direct injection. There are some technical problems to overcome: the entry of the sperm into the egg sets off a number of processes, before ever the nucleic acid contents fuse with that of the egg. But these could be started, in all probability, by the outer cases of spermatozoa, deprived of their DNA. In this way, a woman could be enabled to fertilize herself, a process christened by Professor Rostand 'auto-adultery'. Such a woman would bear a child which was genetically entirely her own, and her husband, if any, might well object that the child was not his and should, therefore, not be allowed to inherit his property. Indeed, he might justifiably refuse to support it.

The logical extension of this proposition is the complete elimination of men and the creation of a race of Amazons. While things will hardly go so far, on earth, it might be convenient to colonize another planet in this way.

Of course, it is already the case that men are present in far larger numbers than is genetically necessary. The semen from a single man would be more than sufficient to fertilize all the women in the country. Probably a single man could, by means of AID and storage, in a single lifetime fertilize every fertile woman in the world, although it is true that, for fertilization to be achieved, considerable numbers of sperm must be present. As the British physiologist Professor A. S. Parkes has observed: 'Women are beginning to have the scarcity value previously held by men. Biologically . . . there are something like a million tons of unnecessary male biomass in this country alone.' This is extremely inefficient, at least in the language of productivity, and unless men genuinely have something the others haven't got, outside sex, some shifting of the ratio between the sexes, by methods discussed in the previous chapter, could become a matter of policy.

Some scientists, it is true, are sceptical of the practicability of such developments. For instance, Dr Max Perutz, who shared a Nobel award for his work at Cambridge on the structure of proteins, told a reporter: 'I fail to visualize how you are going to perform surgery on the genetic apparatus of man. . . . The number of nucleotide base-pairs in a single human germ cell is of the order of 1000 million, distributed over 46 chromosomes. How could we delete a specific gene from a single chromosome, or add specific genes to it, or repair a mistake consisting of a single nucleotide pair in one gene? It hardly seems possible.' But, as we have seen, the problem need not present itself in such uncompromising terms, and Perutz himself makes the qualification that 'conceivably methods of transduction will become feasible; we may find harmless viruses which can be introduced into man and used to transduce desirable genes into people who lack them.'

But Marshall W. Nirenberg, a leading biochemical geneticist who was one of the first to achieve the assembly of a simple nucleic acid in the test-tube, is still more confident. Pointing out that 'genetic surgery, applied to micro-organisms, is a reality,' he declares: 'I have little doubt that the obstacles will eventually be overcome. The only question is when. My guess is that cells will be programmed with synthesized messages within 25 years. If efforts along these lines were intensified, bacteria might be programmed within five years.' And he adds: 'The point which deserves special emphasis is that man may be able to program his own cells with synthesized information long before he will be able to assess adequately the long-term consequences of such alterations, long before he will be able to formulate goals, and long before he can resolve the ethical and moral problems which will be raised.'

Professor Tatum, likewise, considers that 'We can be optimistic about long-range possibilities of therapy by the design and synthesis and introduction of new genes or gene products into cells of defective organs', while Joshua Lederberg of California Institute of Technology, in a broadcast, gave it as his opinion that 'with a fairly strenuous effort' we might manage such tinkering with heredity in ten or twenty years.

That seems soon enough, and the question of how we should handle such powers – indeed whether we dare use them at all – is one we should begin to consider.

Such work opens up practical prospects at which the imagination boggles. While cloning methods could duplicate Derby winners in-definitely, genetic surgery could push up their speeds until they no longer looked like horses.

From making nonsense of sporting events in the animal world, it would be but a short step to making nonsense of human sporting events. Athletics could become a battle between geneticists, each seeking to endow his DNA with outstanding athletic properties. Given cloning as well, we may expect to see races in which every competitor crosses the finishing line at the same moment. And this is merely the physical aspect. The personnel selection boards of the future will work with a gene-map of the candidates, and a box of dice.

Professor Lederberg believes that the first step may be to implant human cell nuclei into animals, perhaps apes, and thus to produce hybrids; the next step will be to push this process further, incorporating organs and limbs of human origin in animals. These animal experiments, he believes, will be 'pushed in steps as far as biology will allow' because of the 'touchiness of experimentation on obviously human material'. He makes clear that he does not advocate such experiments; indeed he fears that they may be tried without 'even an adequate understanding of human values, not to mention vast gaps in human genetics'. This makes it essential to think out the implications beforehand, otherwise policies may be adopted under the influence of the first publicly known results. Opinion may be unduly influenced by such factors as whether these first para-humans look attractive or gruesome, in popular terms. It is perhaps at this point that the layman may begin to say with Sir Macfarlane Burnet, 'there are dangers in knowing what should not be known'. As the *New Scientist* observed in a similar context, 'Rules, perhaps laws, will be needed to allow for, say, treatment of congenitally malformed children, while excluding the temptation to "improve" nature in socially undesirable ways.'

The 'man-farming biologist', in Professor Rostand's phrase, may be the most controversial figure of the immediate future.

But if all this seems too much to take seriously, we should at least face the fact that a very considerable power of intervention in heredity lies at our disposal right now, following the recent discoveries of germ-cell storage and inovulation, and the imminent achievement of *in vitro* fertilization, described in Chapter 2. Eugenics has suddenly become a realistic issue.

The new eugenics

Some scientists feel strongly that we should employ these new techniques without delay. As the late Herman J. Muller, of Indiana University, one of the earliest workers in the field of genetics, has emphatically said:

> The means exist right now of achieving a much greater, speedier and more significant genetic improvement of the population, by the use of selection, than could be effected by the most sophisticated methods of

treatment of the genetic material that might be available in the twenty-first century.

Eugenics is sometimes regarded as divided into 'negative eugenics' and 'positive eugenics'. Negative eugenics consists of the elimination of undesirable features, and especially the biochemical defects which are known to be propagated by a single damaged or defective gene. In addition to hemophilia, there are several severe diseases – many of them so handicapping that they tend to eliminate themselves. Thus some children are born without the ability to manufacture the substance gamma-globulin, from which the antibodies of the immune system are made. Such children are wholly unable to resist infection and, until the discovery of antibiotics, died in the first weeks of life from one infection or another. Other children are unable to break up a substance known as phenylalanine, present in many varieties of food. If untreated, they become idiots, unable to feed or clean themselves, and are unlikely ever to reach the point of having children. Today, the condition can be detected and such children can be placed on a special diet, devoid of phenylalanine, when they develop normally and may even develop some ability to tolerate phenylalanine. Similarly, there are children who cannot tolerate certain natural sugars.

Though such children now survive, they may transmit the defective gene to their offspring, if they have any. Such a defect can rather rapidly spread through a population, as is shown by the case of the way in which the disease known as Huntington's chorea was introduced into the North American continent. This disease usually does not strike until after the reproductive age, so it does not tend to be bred out. It leads to progressive muscular and mental deterioration over a period of ten or twenty years, ending in a gruesome death. In the seventeenth century, six people with this condition arrived in America. When a survey was made in 1916, 962 cases could be identified, including those no longer alive, and the way in which the gene had spread across the country from east to west, with steps of one or more generations on the way, could be traced. None of these 962 people need have suffered if the original half dozen could have been persuaded not to procreate.

To discourage people carrying a known defect from transmitting it is clearly desirable. Moreover, if this can be done consistently, the defective gene will, at the end of one generation, vanish from the gene-pool. Thereafter the problem ceases to exist: perhaps, very occasionally, a new case may crop up, as a result of mutation, and will have to be dealt with in the same way. Substantially, however, the defect has been eliminated.

Today sensitive tests for most of these conditions exist, so marriage counselling is feasible. Advice of this kind is no doubt already given by some doctors in civilized countries: but there is no compulsion to take it, and some cases may not come to the doctors' attention.

The case is simple when the defect is so clear-cut and there are no obviously desirable 'good' genes in the same heredity. It would be harder to know whether one should discourage an Einstein or a Bach from procreating simply because he suffered from hemophilia or phenylketonuria. It is yet harder when we consider more generalized defects, let us say low intelligence, which are probably the outcome of many genes, some of which may well be associated with desirable characteristics. Should we discourage a poet like Rimbaud from procreating because we disapprove of his moral character?

In asking this question, we have really moved into the area of positive eugenics, since to discourage the propagation of low intelligence is the same as to encourage the propagation of high intelligence.

The difficulty in making use of the new techniques is that we have no methods of measuring mental characteristics, other than intelligence (in the narrow sense), and it is precisely these in which we are most interested. Nor do we know how they are connected genetically, so that we run the risk of breeding out one characteristic in our attempts to breed in another. According to the doubtless apocryphal story, when the dancer Isadora Duncan proposed to George Bernard Shaw that they should have a baby, arguing, 'Think of a child with my body and your mind,' he declined, saying, 'Ah, but suppose it had *my* body and *your* mind!' The animal or plant breeder can throw away his poor results, but human beings cannot so easily do so.

Until the day of gene surgery, therefore, eugenics must be a hit-and-miss business. Even so, it might be advantageous to a country, or any large group of people, to encourage selection, since subjective judgments are not without value and on the whole the genetic standard would tend to rise. Indeed, there are some who believe that it is currently deteriorating and that the people with poorer heredity are procreating more numerously than those with good heredity. Dr William Shockley, famous as the inventor of the transistor, believes that this deterioration can be coupled with war and famine as the third great world problem. As we have no means of measuring total heredity, or of comparing the value of one trait with another, such a contention is impossible to prove. But if it is true it certainly makes the case for some kind of eugenic policy even stronger.

But it is unlikely that any western country will introduce compulsion. They are not even likely to move with any speed towards a permissive situation. On a matter which could arouse strong feelings, no democratic government is going to risk loss of votes until it becomes clear that a substantial section of the electorate is firmly in favour of such a move. They have already shown themselves reluctant to encourage or discourage procreation differentially in various social groups.

The most plausible solution, which has been hotly advocated by Herman Muller, is one sometimes known as 'germinal choice'. It is proposed that germ-cell banks be established containing a variety of types of semen, to which people can apply, stating what characteristics they personally would hope to see in their offspring. They would then be supplied with semen derived from donors having such characteristics. 'As an aid in making these choices there would be provided as full documentation as possible concerning the donors of the germinal material, the lives they had led, and their relatives. The couples con-cerned would also have advice available from geneticists, physicians, psychologists, experts in the fields of activity of the donors being con-sidered, and other relevant specialists, as well as generalizers.' The donors would of course be anonymous and preferably no longer living, so that personality cultism and personal complications would be prevented.

It seems reasonable to suppose that a number of progressive people would take advantage of such a facility, at least in the case of some of their children, even where they were themselves perfectly fertile, and for in-fertile persons it would be an obvious course. They would be motivated as much by the desire of having above-average children (and this is a strong motivation) as by public spirit. Such a trend would develop slowly at first, no doubt, but if, after a generation, it became clear that such 'pre-adopted' children – to use Sir Julian Huxley's term for it – were really above average, the practice might develop very rapidly.

The idea of germinal choice now dates back thirty years or more – at one time it was called by the highly discouraging name of eutelegenesis –

and various people have attempted to draw up lists of desirable qualities. Muller, for instance, named such desirable qualities as moral courage and co-operative disposition, appreciation of nature and aptness of expression. But there is much evidence that these are the product at least as much of environment as of heredity.

Today the note is changing from one of advice to one of warning. Leder-berg, for instance, fears that decisions may be taken hastily, on the basis of popular approval or disapproval of particular individuals who lend themselves to eugenic or other biological experiments.

However, Dr Bronowski has pointed out that 'multiplication of what we choose to call the fit can really have very little effect on the presence of recessives' – that is, of those genes which only show up when both parents carry them. Long ago, J. B. S. Haldane used the same argument to show that sterilization of the unfit, which was then being advocated, would not in fact eliminate the qualities objected to.

Professor Luria, while discounting the notion that genetics promises either a millennium or enslavement, told fellow biologists at a meeting two years ago: 'What we, in anticipation of the remarkable advances that may soon be forthcoming, can do is to attempt to create some machinery by which the social implications of our work can be debated rationally and openly, so that any important decision as to its application can be arrived at by an informed and well-advised public. I would not think it premature, for example, for the United Nations as well as the National Academy of Sciences of the United States to establish committees on the genetic direction of human heredity.'

So far, neither organization has shown any signs of taking the hint.

But the simple plan of germinal selection does not really come to grips with the issues, as Dr Lederberg has pointed out. Changing the genetic constitution of man is a slow business and the question is, what will he need in the future, rather than what does he need now. To take a crude instance, evolution has developed in man elaborate defences against invasion by germs but has provided almost no defences against chemical attack. But in the modern world, with its growing range of antiseptics, antibiotics and so on, infection is decreasingly important. On the other hand, chemical pollution of the environment is increasing rapidly. The genetic engineer needs to consider whether he could not introduce quite new capacities to meet this hazard.

Again, evolution depends upon procreation and selects people so that they have a maximum chance of surviving to procreative age; with minor exceptions, it is unable to influence, or be influenced by, what they do after production of offspring ceases – and this is why we are so poor at resisting the ravages of age. But in the modern world, in which half the life span may be spent after bringing up one's offspring, this is no longer good enough. We therefore need to equip man with genes which will serve him in later life, and as life span is extended, the need will grow.

Lederberg thus offers us a glimpse of a future in which man will control his own evolution in a far more radical way than was even dreamed of until genetic engineering became, anyway, a theoretical possibility. Remote as it may seem now, when even conventional eugenics is still viewed askance, it needs only successful demonstration of such techniques in animal breeding for the question of their application to man to begin to be raised in earnest.

Family plan

The proposition that we should inaugurate genetic policies right away raises a host of social questions which geneticists like Muller skate quickly over or ignore, but a number of them have been pinpointed by Professor Kingsley Davis of the University of California at Berkeley.

A state or national pedigree board would be required to decide who were to be donors. The natural desire of most people to bear their own children would lead to bootlegging of spermatozoa and possibly eggs, and, to make the programme work, non-donors – the bulk of the population – would probably have to be sterilized. But perhaps women of good hormonal constitution would be needed to serve as hosts or adoptive mothers to implanted, fertilized eggs. Whether people would learn to accept non-biological children as their own, as fully as they do their biological children, is an unanswered question.

Donors, presumably, would be free to produce biological children and this would make them an élite group. It would be a matter of status to belong and bribery, evasion and sperm-substitution would occur. The question of whether all couples are equally fit to bring up children would also arise, since the adult (as the psychologists and anthropologists have so forcibly argued) is the product of environment as well as of heredity.

Furthermore, it is difficult to see why the sterilized individuals should be held to monogamy, or even why those adjudged unsuitable to rear children should trouble to maintain any domestic life at all. The family is already being eroded by the intervention of school and state, and this might be its *coup de grâce*.

As Dr Robert S. Morison of Cornell puts it: 'Once sex and reproduction are separated, society will have to struggle with . . . defining the nature of interpersonal relationships which have no long-term social point . . . [and] seek new ways to ensure reasonable care for infants and children in an emotional atmosphere which lacks biological reinforcement. . . .' The language is a bit abstract, but the point is a strong one.

But the fact is, people are very much committed to the maintenance of the family, which remains an important source of emotional rewards and of security. They are unlikely to give voting approval for any plan which threatens to demolish it. As Kingsley Davis says, 'An effective system of eugenic control would involve profound changes in the very web of relations that organizes and expresses the personal lives of moderns. It would overthrow the existing system of emotional rewards and punishments, the present interpretations of reality, the familiar links between the person and social status.' And he concludes, as I do, that the introduction of genetic control in the near future, though theoretically possible, is unlikely.

But that is not the whole story. We are faced, as a result of medical progress, with a population explosion the violence of which is still not generally understood. Many believe that new scientific methods of agriculture, including sea-farming and the conversion of inorganic substances like petroleum to protein, will suffice to feed the additional mouths. But even if we leave aside the social consequences of an excessive population density, and the frustrations and disturbances of body-chemistry which result, it is clear that the projected populations cannot be fed. In mid-1967 President Johnson received reports showing that world-wide famines are inevitable before food production can possibly catch up. The question, therefore, of regulating the right to reproduce is certain to arise, quite apart from eugenic considerations.

Today the idea of licensing procreation still gives rise to merriment or ridicule. Our laws and our morals were evolved in a period when to increase the population was a prime necessity: they go back to the 'Be fruitful and multiply' of the Bible. Abortion is both a theological sin and in most countries a legal crime. Birth-control, where it is allowed, is allowed as a matter of private convenience, rarely as a matter of public policy. Marriage is an 'unlimited franchise to procreate'.

Meanwhile, we have eliminated many of the forces which selected the strong from the weak, and are coasting on the genetic selection of the past.

It is virtually certain that this total failure to face the biological realities created by our own scientific advances will cause such disaster that there will be a sudden reversal of policy. And once the right to bear children comes under regulation, the use of those powers to improve the genetic stock rather than to degrade it could follow relatively easily. Our current system of marital selection, based on propinquity and sexual attractiveness, is not so startlingly successful that it can withstand all assaults. In short, it must be concluded that, sooner or later, genetic regulation will be adopted.

This does not mean that it will be adopted in Britain, the U.S.A. or even in Western Europe or the Commonwealth. It seems more likely that some eastern country will be the first to try the experiment – it might well be China. If it is seen to bestow advantages, the countries which are slow to make social experiments may be driven to follow.

It is curious to reflect that the great spiritual philosopher, J. E. Renan, in his *Dialogues*, saw in eugenics a transcendent possibility. 'A far-reaching application of physiology and of the principle of selection,' he said as long ago as 1871, 'might lead to the creation of a superior race, whose right to govern would reside not only in its science, but in the very superiority of its blood, its brain, its nervous system.' There would be joy in submitting to them, he said, for they would be 'incarnations of the divine'. Perhaps, after all, it will be the French who first introduce positive eugenics.

There is, apart from this, one type of genetic intervention which might be adopted with much less pother.

Eliminating defects

Must people with genetic defects resign themselves, if they have a public conscience, to childlessness? Is there no prospect, short of complete DNA replacement by such methods as have been sketched, of correcting any defect? It looks as if there is.

Since approximately four per cent of all births display signs of genetic defect – about 160,000 annually in the U.S.A. – the point is not a minor one.

One could take eggs and sperms from a pair of individuals wishing to procreate, one of whom carried a defect of this kind, and achieve fertilization in the test-tube. The fertilized eggs would then be allowed to develop to a point at which it could be determined whether or not any of them carried the defect. The defective ones could then be destroyed, and one of the satisfactory ones could be reimplanted in the mother's uterus, to be brought to term in the normal way. At present there are no fully developed techniques for identifying the presence of defects at a very early stage. Presumably the embryo would have to develop to the point at which a number of cells could be separated from it without damage for enzymatic investigation. Or, more probably, after the egg had divided once, the two daughter cells would be separated and allowed to grow on normally: a little later, when there were enough cells to provide sufficient material for analysis, one could be investigated by mincing up the cells and looking for the enzyme in question. If it was satisfactory, its twin could then be reimplanted.

That eggs can thus be made to twin, without ill effect, is well established; what is still doubtful is whether the embryo can be successfully reimplanted after it has reached a size adequate for enzymatic investigation. If not, probably one of the pair could be held back in development by cooling until such time as the other had been investigated.

The necessity of destroying the defective embryos, which constitutes abortion under present law in many countries, will no doubt arouse resistance. Those countries which do not consider destruction of the embryo to be abortion until after the fifth month of pregnancy, or some other stated period, will then be at an advantage.

Because of this consideration, it would be attractive if one could pick over the unfertilized eggs and sperm, identifying the sound ones, rather as the South German wine-growers pick over the grapes and select only the finest for their 'Auslese' (selected) wines. The selected germ-cells could then be fertilized in the test-tube and the embryo implanted, or the egg could be implanted and fertilized by AID. Unfortunately, no techniques are at present in view, as far as I am aware, by which defective germ-cells could be identified. Much larger quantities of material than these invisible motes are required, at present. Procreation by 'Auslese' embryos, on the other hand, is a distinct possibility.

In addition to the use of techniques of the kind described to alter germ-cells and thus the whole hereditary line, there is also the possibility of using them to correct defects in individuals after they have been born, i.e. to tinker with body-cells. This kind of intervention has been termed euthenics, or euphenics, in contrast with eugenics. Thus, if a man was born with defective liver cells, lacking some needed enzyme, it might be possible to extract one or two liver cells, modify the DNA in them, and reimplant them, at the same time excising most of the liver. Since this organ has remarkable powers of regeneration, the implanted cells would soon replace all the excised faulty tissue with new and faultless tissue.

Such techniques might eventually be extended to mongolism, colour-blindness, cystic fibrosis and a couple of dozen more defects. Tatum thinks this the most promising of the possible lines of approach.

And there is one possibility which could bump this line of research up into the 'top-priority' class very quickly: an increase in the background radiation due to fall-out from atomic explosions or, still worse, the direct effect of the explosions themselves. As Professor Bentley Glass has observed: 'All the genetic experiments ever conducted, including one conducting in my own laboratory with a dose of no more than five roentgens [units of radiation], indicate that there is a direct linear proportionality between the dose of radiation and the frequency of mutations produced.' In other words, there is no threshold below which the effect is absent. The rate is probably doubled for every 60 roentgens, or thereabouts, and existing fall-out has already put the rate up by more than a quarter. Throughout the world, at a rough guess, ten thousand defective children are born annually as a direct result of fall-out, more than half of them in countries, such as India, not involved in nuclear testing. The rain falls on the just and on the unjust alike.

In the event of even a limited war, the rate would rise steeply. Nor need we delude ourselves with the belief that there are 'clean' bombs. Though fusion bombs produce fewer of the short-lived radioactive products, such as strontium-90, iodine-131 and cesium-137, they produce much more of the persistent carbon-14 which hangs around for thousands of years and enters into the basic materials of which living things are made. According to eminent geneticists, the defects caused in future generations by the carbon-14 already released will eventually outnumber those caused by all other components of fall-out by two to one.

The ethics of imposing such damage on the innocent bystander and even on future generations are indefensible. The least that any nation involved in such testing can do is to press forward with finding methods of repair regardless of cost. But so far the point has not been taken. Such are the costs of turning a blind eye to biological research.

The spectre of gene warfare

Professor Tatum sees gene repair as also providing a major therapeutic measure in cancer. Yet, while most biologists have been fundamentally optimistic about the possible uses of genetic engineering, Professor Salvador Luria of MIT has declared that his reaction has 'not been a feel-ing of optimism but one of tremendous fear of the potential dangers that genetic surgery, once it becomes feasible, can create if misapplied.' He points out that a negative genetic surgery may be developed. For example, fruit flies are liable to be infected by a virus which changes their constitu-tion so that they become highly sensitive to the simple gas carbon dioxide. Suddenly it becomes a deadly poison to them.

How, asks Professor Luria, would one cope with a similar situation if it arose in relation to man – if someone devises a virus which sensitizes man to some substance and then quietly disseminates the virus throughout the world? After everyone has, unwittingly, become affected, the aggressor announces what he has done and threatens to release the substance to which *everyone*, except his own people, is now sensitive, unless his demands are met.

'Someone could gain a tremendous control over humanity by spreading such a terrible object, thereby holding the power of life and death over a large number of human beings.' And holding it indefinitely, one might add. 'This is an extreme and horrible example, almost science fiction matter, but it emphasizes the kind of thing which has been in my mind every time I have thought about the possibility of genetic surgery and engineering.'

Society – including geneticists – is not adapted to cope with such a situation. Can society learn to control aggression before such a danger arises? Few will be so optimistic as to think so.

Moreover, we must think in terms of the modern concept of the 'undeclared war'. Since the term is probably unfamiliar, a little preliminary explanation may be called for.

In current thinking, the best way to wage war is to wage it without your enemy even being aware that it is happening. If, for example, you can control the weather so as to ensure poor crops for your enemy and good ones for yourself, in the course of years you will gradually improve the position of your country relative to his. Then perhaps you could quietly introduce a few crop diseases – nothing dramatic which would lead to suspicion, just a slight rise here and there apparently from some natural cause. And why stop at plant or stock diseases? Some minor human epidemics might help. Even the common cold keeps people away from work. It might be ten years or more before it dawned on the health authorities that they were really being *too* unlucky with minor illnesses. Meanwhile you inflate your own statistics a little, to avoid odious comparisons. And, of course, this is merely the biological side. Industrial disputes, insurance losses, the draining away of brain-power, and a thousand other things will help to undermine the strength of a country. Even a narrow-minded regime, an obfuscating religion, can prevent a country's progress. And who knows whether this is just a speculation? Perhaps there are nations consciously waging this kind of warfare now.

In this context, it would be obviously extremely useful if you could – as well as trying to improve the genetic character of your own people – enfeeble the heredity of your enemy. Nothing so obvious, perhaps, as sending people with actual genetic defects to intermarry and spread the damaged gene among his population: the results of such a policy might be too easily detected. Something more in the line of encouraging the more intelligent or skilful people not to breed.

Or perhaps actual gene warfare. If viruses can be used to carry new genetic material into cells, perhaps one could tamper with the genes of another nation without their ever realizing the fact. History would simply record, as it has so often done in the past, that such-and-such a nation rose to power while certain other countries entered a decline.

On this gloomy note I must end this survey of genetic prospects.

When French philosophers met at Grenoble in 1954, they discussed the extent to which the human body was becoming a chattel, a possession on a par with one's car or one's television set. The jurist, Aurel David, with remarkable foresight, stated the problem in these terms: 'To what principle shall we appeal in deciding what is desirable, acceptable, legitimate? Upon what criterion shall we base choices that will commit the future? How shall we contrive to exercise the formidable powers allotted to us by science with a minimum of decency and dignity?' It is a set of questions for which, today, we still have no satisfactory answers.

7

Can We Create Life?

The alchemists of old dreamed of creating life in the retort. A homunculus – a miniature man – would appear from the appropriate mixture and somehow grow to full size, though what one would then do with him was not usually discussed. The famous sixteenth-century doctor, Paracelsus, standing at the mid-point between alchemy and science, proposed a technique involving the warming of human semen and feeding it with human blood. If you do this, after 80 days you will have, he said, 'a true and living infant, having all the members of a child that is born of a woman, but much smaller. This we call a homunculus.' He perceived the social problem also, for he added: 'It should afterwards be educated with the greatest care and zeal until it grows up and begins to display intelligence.'

This, however, was not so much creating life from inert chemicals as fostering the material nature had, in her own mysterious way, prepared. These two alternative approaches face us again today.

The same dream intrigued Mary Shelley, more than a century and a half ago. With remarkable prescience, she foresaw the truly scientific creation of a living being of human type – a humanoid, as we should now say – by a scientist. The scientist in her novel was called Frankenstein, and the word has become synonymous with the monster he produced.

That was a flight of fancy, but today scientists are becoming confident that life can be created. For instance, Professor J. D. Bernal, the man who more than thirty years ago launched the use of physical methods in studying the structure of living material, has recently declared: 'Life is beginning to cease to be a mystery, and becoming practically a cryptogram, a puzzle, a code that can be broken, a working model that can sooner or later be made.'

To the layman, the notion of creating life may seem wildly impossible, a mere flight of fancy; or, if he thinks it possible, it seems arrogant or even impious. Both attitudes were dramatically challenged in 1965 when Professor Charles Price, the newly elected President of the American Chemical Society, publicly proposed that the synthesis of life be made an American national goal. In a letter addressed to the heads of the National Science Foundation, the National Institutes of Health, the Atomic Energy Commission, the National Aeronautics and Space Administration, and the Chemical Committee of the National Academy of Sciences, he proposed a twenty-year effort involving a quarter to a half of the nation's scientific manpower. 'All responded favourably,' he said later – though the A.C.S. was at pains to make it clear he was not speaking for the society. Work, he thought, would probably begin with the synthesis of important components of living systems. The next steps would be to synthesize viruses, then the sub-units of which cells are made, then whole cells and finally multi-celled organisms.

At the time, many people took this to mean 'synthesizing human beings'. In fact, Professor Price says he had a couple of orders from his sailing crew for Liz Taylor and Brigitte Bardot. But in a later comment, he made it clear that he believed the level of synthesis involved in creating intelligence would be at least as big a step beyond creating a living system as creating the system would be for us in the first place. However, though it would take much longer, he couldn't imagine that this would not happen in 'a century or so'.

When I went to see him in his laboratory in the University of Pennsylvania, I asked him why he had been moved to make such a proposal at this particular time. 'I feel that chemists in this country need the stimulus of a major goal, to which their work can contribute,' he said to me. 'They need a goal which will stimulate them and give them a sense of specific purpose, in the kind of way that the landing of a man on the moon has stimulated engineering and electronics research.'

But he also stressed the indirect advantages. 'For example,' he said, 'if you can find out enough about how membranes are put together and how they work, you might be able to make an artificial kidney that wouldn't take up most of the room.'

Professor Price also speculated on the possibility of making living systems of a new kind. As he pointed out, when a chemist talks about making synthetic rubber, he does not necessarily mean that he wants to copy natural rubber. He wants to make something, if possible, even more rubbery, and is prepared to adopt a completely different chemical structure from the natural one to get it. So 'when we understand the nature of the living process as a total system, we might be able to design other kinds of systems which would have the general characteristics of living systems, and especially the ones we would like to use.' This he calls 'one of the most challenging prospects I can imagine'.

One of those who took Professor Price's lead seriously was Dr Carl Berkley, who, in a leading article in *Medical Research Engineering*, took the view that even on the basis of present technical knowledge we could *right now* produce a system which would meet the basic criteria for life, even though it would not be a biological system. That is to say, it would be able to duplicate itself, to restore a normal internal equilibrium when some external force disturbed it (homeostasis) and to adapt. Such a system would be much larger than any biological living system and, though entirely mechanical, would be alive. The question he put to his readers was: 'Is this worth doing?'

The engineering challenge thus raised is surely intriguing, but it is the biological variety of life which most scientists have in mind when they raise this issue, and it is that which I shall now discuss.

What makes scientists believe that they could achieve such a goal, and what precisely do they have in mind? Though the prospects of success are further off than most of the projects we have so far considered, the possibility is so extraordinary that it deserves close examination. If to control man's evolution represents a turningpoint in the history of the human race, how are we to describe the creation of life? Since it includes the former, it must be adjudged an even more farreaching development. And, in view of Price's proposal, now may be the time to consider whether we should even start on such a course, which is bound to be costly in the execution and might in the end prove even more costly in a victory.

The programme which Paracelsus claimed to know about – the cultivation of men in the laboratory, starting from human materials such as semen or eggs – we have already discussed and seen to be probable of achievement. Even so orthodox a biologist as Professor Bentley Glass has forecast that we may discover 'how to cultivate the reproductive cells of men and animals, to produce normal human embryos, and to raise them, either in artificial cultures or in foster mothers . . . and in the process may find out how to modify defective genes or replace them.' But the syn-thesis of life from definitely non-living chemical materials is something else again.

If the programme seems to the non-scientific reader beyond the bounds of possibility, it is probably because of his understanding of the word 'life' and a misconception of the processes which it denotes.

Many people still think of life in somewhat mystical terms as a mys-terious gift breathed into inanimate matter suddenly making it animate. The scientist sees a living organism simply as a machine – an enormously complex and subtle machine capable of responses and adjustments no man-made machine is yet capable of, yet a machine nevertheless. He is entirely confident that, if once he can put the bits together correctly, the machine will start to tick, just as a watchmaker does not doubt that the watch he is making will start to run as soon as the parts are assembled. And he also believes the converse of this proposition: that if the parts are *not* put together correctly, or if essential parts are missing, no amount of breathing, no possible miracle, will inspire the dull clay to live.

He holds this to be just as true of man as of less highly evolved animals. Man is no longer seen, as he generally was in the nineteenth century and earlier, as having a special place in nature and being uniquely dis-tinguished from all other living things. His more elaborate brain and consequent powers of speech and abstract thought may put him ahead of other creatures, but he stands above them on the same ladder.

The scientists' confidence in what may be called the mechanical nature of living systems and in the essential possibility of being able to duplicate these mechanisms springs from the success of a number of experiments in which attempts have been made to duplicate some of the steps in the chain between the inanimate and the animate. Of these, perhaps the most striking is the creation of viruses.

Making a virus

At the threshold of the ladder of living things stands the virus – a tiny structure possessing the power to multiply itself indefinitely, and to under-go mutation, yet not itself carrying out chemical processes, or consuming nutrients and excreting waste products. Put crudely, it reproduces, but it doesn't eat and it doesn't breathe. It consists of a hereditary message, coded into nucleic acid, specifying how to make a virus, but it borrows the cell machinery of bacterial or other cells to do the work for it. Needing, there-fore, no cellular machinery it consists simply of the nucleic acid message with a protective coat of protein. (Some viruses are slightly more compli-cated: they may have special equipment for squirting the nucleic acid into the cell which is to perform the task of making more virus, for instance, or enzymes which facilitate escape of the new viruses from the cell, and so on.)

When you stop to think of it, this is quite an extraordinary thing. It is rather as if a computer tape should wander round inserting itself into computers for no other purpose than to get them to print out more com-puter tapes like itself – incidentally, often wrecking the computer in the process.

Back in the thirties, when biologists were first trying to isolate these invisibly small particles (you can't see them in a light microscope, the only kind available at that time), they were uncertain what they were deal-ing with. The fact that masses of them could be induced to crystallize, as sugar does, suggested that they were inanimate, while their power to multiply seemed to prove the opposite.

Some scientists believe viruses derive from bacteria which have dis-carded their cellular equipment and become, as it were, parasites. Others think they may have arisen spontaneously. Are they living things on the way down, or inanimate things on the way up? We may never know.

Whether you regard them as alive or not, man has discovered how to make them. In 1965, a team at the University of Illinois, under Professor Sol Spiegelman, in a brilliant series of experiments, succeeded in putting together the non-living nucleic-acid message which produced a virus which would go on and multiply indefinitely. Their artificial virus was completely indistinguishable from a natural virus.

The virus on which they worked, known as φ-beta, is a small, many-sided particle, containing an RNA-chain of about 3000 units, which battens on bacterial cells.

The difficulties of the experiment did not consist in getting the parts to assemble themselves – they do this with the greatest enthusiasm – but in fishing the bits out in the first place and making sure that the mixture did not contain any natural virus. The secret of the task was to obtain from natural virus the special enzyme, known as a replicase, which it uses to link together the sub-units into nucleic acid. To isolate this in the presence of enzymes which destroy RNA, such as bacteria contain, was a major task.

The replicase speedily assembled nucleotides into RNA of the right weight and density. When this RNA was introduced into bacteria, it proceeded to make new viruses just as infective as the old, and to do it just as well as before.

The immediate prospect emerges of being able to modify the nucleic acid slightly and so to create novel viruses – if anyone should want new viruses. (The most obvious people to want them are presumably the military, though conceivably agriculturists might want viruses which could attack unwanted weeds or pests, without injuring animals and crops, if any such could be found or created.)

However, scientists are chiefly interested because this is a major step towards understanding the life process, and, in particular, towards elucidating the more complicated but essentially similar life process, DNA replication. Spiegelman's achievement is seen by molecular biologists as another important confirmation of their belief that life is imitable. The step to which the team is now addressing itself is to do without the bacterial cell altogether and to achieve the synthesis of virus in the test-tube from nothing but amino acids, nucleotides and replicase.

Spiegelman's achievement derives from an earlier achievement by Heinz Fraenkel-Conrat, a Prussian who left Germany in the year Hitler came to power and has been working in California ever since. Using the RNA-virus which gives mosaic disease to tobacco and certain other plants, he contrived to separate the protein coat from the nucleic acid; each solution, tested on tobacco plants for infectivity, had no effect. Then he mixed the two solutions together, not seriously expecting anything to happen. Within a few moments the appearance of the mixture began to alter, and, when examined with an electron microscope, it was seen to contain perfect tobacco-mosaic viruses. The parts had re-assembled themselves. And when applied to tobacco plants they proved able to infect them in the usual way. At the time this was described as 'Life Created in the Test-Tube' and, if we concede that viruses are to be regarded as alive, it almost was; 'Life Recreated in the Test-Tube' would be more exact. This was in 1955.

The time elapsing between Fraenkel-Conrat's and Spiegelman's work, just ten years, gives us some measure of the rate at which such work develops.

Fraenkel-Conrat *re-assembled* the two main components – or rather they proved able to re-assemble themselves. Spiegelman started with the *raw materials* and showed that they would assemble themselves into one of the components (nucleic acid) which Fraenkel-Conrat used, and this proved capable of manufacturing the other structure (coat-protein) and joining up with it, within a bacterial cell, as it does in nature. This is clearly a major advance. Above all, it shows that such materials have the extraordinary inbuilt property of being able to assemble themselves, in a series of stages. First, raw materials assemble themselves into structures; then the structures assemble themselves into complete viruses.

This is the crucial point. It is precisely because the raw materials of life have this eerie *self-assembling capacity* that scientists feel confident that complex forms of life can also be induced to assemble themselves. The scientist does not really aim to create life; he simply aims to provide the conditions in which life can create itself.

And his belief that life can create itself is linked with the belief that life did once create itself on this planet. Research into the origins of life is the second of the developments which have sparked the ambition of Professor Price and others to create living things.

Life from chemicals

One of the ways of understanding the nature of anything is to find out how it originated. It is for this reason, mainly, that scientists have long been interested in the origins of living things. Darwin's success in establishing the validity of the theory of evolution, while destroying any lingering hopes that higher forms of life could be spontaneously created, simultaneously raised the problem of where the most primitive form could come from. For a time, it was believed that at the bottom of the sea there was a 'protoplasmic sludge' which represented the nascent stage of life, and specimens dredged up from enormous depths by the *Challenger* oceanographic expedition were eagerly examined in the hope that they would reveal this living slime, which had been named in advance *Bathybius haeckeli*. But in vain.

The facts are also important in connection with the question of whether there is life elsewhere in the universe. For if the conditions in which life can originate spontaneously can be determined, then it becomes possible to enquire whether there are other planets where such conditions are likely to exist.

But it is also true that if one can define conditions in which life could spring up spontaneously, one can try to establish those conditions and cause it to do so; and the best test of one's theories is actually to attempt the experiment.

Now the remarkable fact, still scarcely appreciated by the non-scientist, is that in the last thirty years a plausible theory of how life could have originated has been built up and many experiments have been devised and executed to test different parts of it. These have been more successful than their originators dared hope. If scientists have not put the various experiments together so as to produce life from inanimate materials so far, it is only because nature takes millions of years and large quantities of material to achieve her results and scientists do not yet know how to speed up the process sufficiently.

In the early 1950's the Nobelist Harold Urey had a brilliant insight which opened the door to the new conception of the origin of life. He realized that the original atmosphere of the earth must have been devoid of oxygen. It probably contained simple gases like hydrogen, ammonia, water vapour and methane (marsh gas). Later, perhaps carbon monoxide and dioxide and nitrogen were added. This atmosphere must have been much more pervious to ultra-violet light than ours. During the first decades of the century, also, the universal role of proteins in living systems and the way they were constructed of amino acids became clear. Since amino acids are built round molecules of ammonia, it was a natural step to see if amino acids would be formed spontaneously in such an atmosphere. Urey suggested the experiment, which one of his students,

Stanley Miller, performed in 1953. Sure enough, the irradiated gases formed amino acids and other molecules characteristic of life. The scientific world was jerked into attention.

Soon people were trying numerous variants, the use of X-rays, heat and light for varying periods on slightly varying mixtures. Within a few years it was shown that, in this sort of way, the nucleotide units of which nucleic acids are constructed may also be formed; also ATP, the cellular fuel, and even small proteins. The scent was strong; the next question was: how could these units have become linked together?

Though Miller's experiment marked a milestone in scientific attention to the subject, the man who first put the issue squarely was the Russian Academician A. I. Oparin, whose book *The Origin of Life* was published in the early 1930's. Oparin took the view that the organic molecules, formed much as I have outlined, became encapsulated in droplets of a type named co-acervates, which absorb selected substances from the medium round them. Thus isolated from the environment, they would be less exposed to forces which might break them down. Such co-acervates, packed with amino acids and nucleotides, would form the precursors of the living cell, until one day some kind of cell division was achieved. It was therefore another startling confirmation of these speculations when, in 1967, the spontaneous formation of co-acervates in a laboratory solution was reported by simply mixing different proteins.

In Miami, an Institute of Molecular Evolution has recently been set up under Professor Sidney Fox to study these processes. Fox supposes that the primitive soup of organic materials washed over hot volcanic rocks. Some would be trapped in rock depressions, where the heat would evaporate and concentrate the contents. Imitating this sequence of events, he found that a slightly different globule, dubbed a microsphere, is formed when the protein-like material thus made is cooled. These microspheres divide by budding in a manner curiously like bacteria, and even form long chains as bacteria do. In certain conditions the microspheres acquire a double-layered wall. Not only proteins but fatty acids are formed during the synthesis of this 'proteinoid' material.

As Fox says, the main importance of such experiments is that they solve the central question: how could substances which today can only be formed by living things, come into existence without living things?

But between the collection of big molecules in a microsphere and the cell as we know it, with its myriad precise chemical reactions, lies a vast gap. It is that gap which these biologists are now attempting to fill.

The primitive cell had to discover how to feed – how to absorb energy from the environment to power its activities. If it can be shown how this was managed, the problem of the origin of life is substantially answered. Professor George Wald of Harvard has argued that this took place in two main stages: the first step must have been fermentation: the breakdown of sugar to simpler components such as alcohol and carbon dioxide, a reaction which yields energy, though at a low efficiency. This is not a difficult trick; yeast does it all the time. But such a process would gradually use up the available sugar-fuel. At some point the sun's energy had to be trapped. So, before the sugar ran out, the cell – we can now call it that – had to produce chemicals which can trap sunlight and learn to do the complicated chemical trick known as photosynthesis. Professor Wald has made the study of these photochemical substances his life-long speciality.

Many of the stages in the evolution of photosynthesis can be plausibly inferred; and if the formation of photosynthetic pigments, or their precursors, the porphyrins, can be imitated in the laboratory by further experiments which are designed as reconstructions of the past, confidence in this line of argument will be strengthened. Such experiments are now being discussed. The fact that the cells we know today can, in some circumstances, revert to a non-oxygen-using form of metabolism, is another fact which tends to strengthen Wald's speculation. But between a plausible theory and proven fact lies a gap which may be hard to fill.

Once photosynthesis was achieved, the cell would produce oxygen as a by-product and the earth's atmosphere would gradually change to the oxidizing atmosphere we know today, in which life could *not* originate, for its raw materials would speedily be oxidized to destruction. Thus for the older conception of a continuous creation of life, we now have to substitute a third solution: the once-for-all evolution of life from inorganic materials a very long time ago. And since fossils at least two thousand million years old are known it must have happened rather early in the earth's history, soon after temperatures had reached the point at which the process was possible.

Making cells

Even if molecular evolutionists could find some series of treatments which would speed up the selection process so that microspheres would start to metabolize in weeks or months rather than the millions or hundreds of millions of years which it is supposed they originally may have taken, it seems unlikely anyone would want to perform the experiments except just to test the theory. As a method of making life it seems unnecessarily tortuous.

As Professor Price suggests, the next contribution to unravelling the life process is more likely to come from attempts to build the structures within the cell. Much of the contents of the cell consists of a network, or rather a system of flat surfaces, studded with molecules of ribonucleic acid. Is there perhaps some unit which, in the right conditions, promptly assembles itself into such layers? Again, the working areas of the cell are packed with structures known as mitochondria – boat-shaped objects with numerous transverse panels. Here the 'cellular fuel' known as ATP (for adenosine triphosphate) is manufactured in a series of chemical reactions, which is why mitochondria are often called 'the power-houses of the cell'. Some biologists suspect that mitochondria are not made under control of the nucleus but simply divide, like bacteria. The best way to settle such a question is to see if they can be made to divide or reproduce themselves in the absence of a nucleus. The cell contains many other structures, such as the Golgi apparatus, the nucleolus and the aster, whose functions and structure are still far from clear. During the next twenty years biologists will be doing an increasing number of experiments to clear up such obscurities.

Incidentally, in the course of all this, they may find they can make cell-components which are, at least in some respects, actually superior to those which nature makes. It is difficult to foresee what directions such developments might take, and at best wildest guesswork, but one can at least imagine that they might produce muscle filaments with greater contractive power or with a shorter recovery time; blood which could restock the muscles with oxygen more efficiently; or nerve cells which could transmit impulses faster than the nerves we have. Remarkable as our bodies are, they are by no means the last word in development, and they also contain evolutionary left-overs, like the tonsils and the vermiform appendix, which are more trouble than they are worth. The German anatomist Wiedersheim once said that he knew of 107 structures in the body which served no purpose and it has been later observed that any good engineer could design a more efficient one. While that was certainly untrue at the time, the more modest possibility that one could polish up the design a little is no longer unreasonable to envisage.

In the course of time scientists will, whenever they find they can construct one of these bits of equipment in the laboratory, wish to test their home-made imitation by inserting it in a normal cell to see how well it works. The techniques of micro-surgery, by which small parts of the cell can be inserted and removed, are being developed by specialists like Professor M. J. Kopac, of New York University, who has, for instance, developed a successful technique for implanting the nucleolus of one cell into another. When all the cell structures have thus been imitated and proved to work – if ever the day arrives – it will be a natural culmination to try to put the lot together and see if they will function as a cell.

If they do, that might also be called the creation of life – the first creation of a living cell.

The expression 'the creation of life' probably evokes an image of a scientist pouring a selection of chemicals into a vat and waiting until a great mass of protoplasm comes slopping purposefully over the rim. But, as we can now see, the story comes in three or four main chapters. The creation of the raw materials of life – proteins and so on – from inorganic materials. This step has been taken. The construction from these materials of cell components, and from them of a living cell. This has not been done and is not in immediate prospect: it may not even be possible. The development of a cell into a higher organism. This has been done, with natural cells, by Professor Steward, whose work we described in Chapter 2, and in a general sense is done whenever an egg develops into an adult organism. There is no reason to suppose that an artificial cell would not develop likewise; though the cells of multi-celled creatures may be more complex in some not yet understood respect than the cells of unicellular organisms. Thus it may be possible to construct something like a bacterium or an amoeba before it is possible to construct an egg or a cell truly comparable with the body-cells of higher organisms.

Obviously, it would simply be a *tour de force* to attempt, when all these phases of the story have been achieved separately, to go through the whole sequence from inorganic chemicals to living being. The biologist who wants, let us say, adenine for an experiment on the structure of mitochondria will not insist on adenine made by Dr C. Ponnamperuma at the Ames Research Center of NASA by methods which imitate the origins of life. Ordinary adenine from a biological supply house will do as well and cost much less.

How soon?

In short, despite Professor Price's proposal, biologists are not actually engaged in a deliberate attempt to advance to the point where they could create life. They are simply attempting to discover in detail how living things work – primarily, I think, because of the essential fascination of the problem, which surely represents one of the greatest challenges to human ingenuity one could think of, and partly because, in the course of so doing, many problems of more practical interest are made soluble. It is in the nature of science constantly to lead one back to fundamental problems. A bridge-builder's need to know in detail about strength and fatigue of materials leads immediately into studies of the structure of matter. The doctor's desire to combat virus diseases leads to enquiring what a virus is and how it functions, and this in turn raises basic questions concerning the materials of which it is made and their properties.

Nevertheless, as soon as it becomes possible, some biologist will attempt to 'create life' in some sense of the term, not simply for the hell of it, but because the only satisfactory way to verify one's theories and methods is to see if they work. For the man who is trying to see how a clock is constructed, the best test of whether he has understood the principles involved is to build a clock and see if it works. Considerations of national prestige may also work to this end: the creation of life is a 'first' which is bound to cause a stir.

For such purposes, the creation of a single living cell, capable of dividing and multiplying, capable of feeding, metabolizing and excreting, and equipped with some kind of irritability or sensitivity to the environment, is sufficient. It would be a fantastic achievement.

Professor Price sees it as being possible in twenty years. For my part, I consider this to be optimistic. The fantastic successes of molecular biology have bred a degree of confidence not far short of arrogance in many of those who work in this field. The walls which surround the central mystery seem ready to fall down when the blast of the trumpet is sounded. But the history of science suggests that such problems are often harder to unravel than appears on the surface.

Less than a century ago, the protoplasm of the cell was conceived as a kind of foam, and many believed that its properties would soon be adequately explained in terms of simple physical properties such as osmosis and surface tension. The way in which a drop of fluid would suck in a splinter of coated glass, dissolve the coating and then eject the splinter, looked so very like the behaviour of an amoeba in ingesting foodstuffs that it was thought that the same physical principles would explain both. Today, we know that the supposed foam is a finely structured network of molecules, in which other molecules and structures are embedded, each as precisely adapted to its purpose as a machine tool.

But just as biologists underestimated the complexity of what they were looking at then, so may they be underestimating the problem today. Thanks to the electron microscope and other tools, we know a lot about the structures in the cell – but we still know very little about the processes which go on. The rapid strides which have been made in understanding how proteins are synthesized encourage us to overlook the fact that we know nothing about how the chromosomes are caused to divide and are then pulled apart, for instance. Nor do we know much about how the fatty components are made. There are quite probably electric forces within the cell which we have no means of mapping at all. The techniques simply don't exist. They are not even on the horizon.

The problem cannot really be compared with the problem of landing man on the moon. This calls for the extension of known techniques. Better communications systems, more powerful thrusts, tougher materials. But in 1950 we already had radio, rocket propellants and ceramics. To make a valid comparison, we should imagine the President of the Aeronautical Society in about 1890 proposing a twenty-year plan to get to the moon – with no computers to control the operation, no radar tracking and only very primitive radio communication, no aluminium or other light metals, and nothing more advanced than a life-boat rocket in the way of propellants. To be sure, fifty or sixty years bridged the technological gap – but no one could have made a meaningful plan to effect such a bridging at that early date. The most one could have done would have been to increase the research funds available in the sensitive areas. This might have cut down the time lag by ten years.

Today, I would imagine, our range of choice is comparable. We can concentrate effort in the field and solve the problem, if it is soluble, in thirty years; or we can leave it alone, and it may solve itself in forty or fifty.

But while for scientific purposes the synthesis of a living cell is the dazzling achievement to aim at, for the ordinary man the possibility which arouses most interest and trepidation is the manufacture of actual organisms, both normal in appearance and monstrous, and this is likely to be achieved much sooner than the synthesis of a cell. As I have already described, scientists are beginning to construct artificial genetic material and to find ways of introducing genetic material into cells. Long before they have an opportunity to introduce such artificial hereditary messages into synthetic cells, they will have introduced them into natural cells and will have produced both normal and monstrous forms of life. By the time this is achieved with artificial cells, the shock will have worn off.

Consequences

At any level, it seems unlikely that life-synthesis will become a regular practice. If anyone wants living organisms, the simplest and cheapest way to obtain them is by the means which nature has so thoughtfully provided and which we already use. It is a well-worn joke that man possesses the only computer capable of learning from experience which can be mass-produced by unskilled labour. The point might be made even more forcibly of the structure that computer moves around in. Even plants and creatures of no intelligence are unsurpassed at producing more of themselves.

The principal consequences of this work, apart from the confirming of biological hypotheses, are likely to be philosophical rather than practical. Before ever a complete synthesis of life takes place, the increasing interchangeability of living and synthesized material will probably erode the popular feeling that life is uniquely different from non-living matter. The production of partly artificial creatures – and later wholly artificial ones – will make it hard to maintain any longer that life is a phenomenon of mystical significance. Unless, of course, these creatures turn out to be zombies, in some definable way differing from normal creatures – a thing which no scientist anticipates.

True, the overall mystery of why matter has inherent in it the property of forming, spontaneously, living organisms which are capable of evolving into ever subtler forms, remains. But that is another question.

There is no doubt a danger that a general realization of the mechanical nature of living systems – however exquisitely organized they be – may lead to a cheapening of life and a tendency to regard it as expendable and unworthy of respect. How serious this danger will be will depend, I suppose, on how far the general level of intelligence has been improved and on how far educationists have managed to tackle the problem of orientating pupils to the realities of existence instead of stuffing them with facts and techniques. For (need it be said?) no such disrespect for life is justified or justifiable. The test of an aircraft is not how easy it is to make, but how well it performs. How much the more, then, must man be judged by what he does, not by where and what he comes from.

8

The Future, If Any

At a guess, there are about 200,000 biologists in the world, depending to some extent on how you define 'biologist'. The sensual man, reflecting on their hazardous activities, may well feel a sense of apprehension. The prospect of having to cope with a number of such innovations simultaneously takes on a nightmare quality, and prompts the question: is this all really a load of nonsense, mere science fiction divorced from present reality? And even if these procedures are technically possible, will they ever be more than laboratory curiosities?

If so, he has missed the point. We are not simply discussing a number of new procedures, but the fact that a revolution is occurring in biology. The things I have described are merely the salient points, the first-fruits of a breakthrough on a broad front. Naturally, biology still has numerous unsolved problems, just as physics has. But the degree of control now being achieved calls for a new relationship between biology and society. Just as physics and chemistry did in the past century, it will steadily bring about a totally new pattern of existence. Whether it will be a happier and more satisfying pattern is by no means obvious, and it is not even clear whether society can survive the strains which will be imposed.

Jacques Piccard, son of the inventor of the deep-diving bathyscaphe, told a symposium at the Stevens Institute at Hoboken, New Jersey, recently that he was 'seriously doubtful' whether mankind would last out the century. Aside from the atomic threat, he stressed the 'widespread, suicidal pollution affecting the air we breathe, the water we drink and the land we till'. Our whole technology was to blame, he said. Superimposed on these stresses, the social stresses created by biology may prove a sizeable final straw.

The question of how soon they will be upon us therefore deserves care-ful attention.

Naturally, no one can predict the future with certitude and no doubt some of the advances about which we are now optimistic will prove impossible, or at any rate the solution will be found so far in the future as to be of little practical importance to us now. But it is equally certain that many of these advances will occur in the very near future. Indeed, many of the techniques described in Chapter 2, such as artificial in-ovulation, are available now. And as I write these lines comes news of a breakthrough on the transplantation front. Dr G. J. V. Nossal, the new director of the Walter and Eliza Hall Institute of Medical Research in Melbourne, has reported a method of desensitizing the body to specific foreign materials by injecting ever smaller pieces of the antigen. It appears that the extent of the immune response is related to the size of the invading molecules. But once the body has met a fragment of the antigen so small that the immune response does not occur, it subsequently ceases to produce antibody to the complete antigen molecule. On the strength of this, Nossal considers that organ transplantation can be perfected in the 1970's, with control of cancer and other diseases following a decade or two later. He has called for a world-wide effort to purify antigens, to see if a mole-cule sufficiently small, and of the right structure to set up tolerance, can be developed. 'If it does,' he told the First International Congress of the Transplantation Society, 'the stage is set for experiments in human beings to see if injection of antigens can induce tolerance in a transplant patient.' There are also encouraging reports about tissue typing and anti-lympho-cytic serum.

On the other hand, I would not personally place any sizeable bet on success in prolonging life, and, while I think it may well be pos-sible to improve memory, I am somewhat sceptical of the possibility of transferring entire memories. Against this, the very recent discovery of a factor controlling nerve growth makes it look extremely probable that we could do something quite drastic about raising intelligence, provided treatment can be given in the foetal stage or the earliest weeks of life.

On pages 204–5, I have ranged the possibilities in three groups: discoveries which are going to affect us within the next five or ten years, if they have not already begun to do so; those which should become practicable within some fifty years; and those which are remoter.

The group which affects all of us, and on which no delay can be brooked, includes, in addition to transplantation techniques, partheno‑ genetic birth, prolonged storage of human eggs and spermatozoa, arrested death, choice of sex of offspring and the mind‑modifying drugs. Surely enough to cope with.

In phase two, I forecast, we shall see all these problems become more acute, with hibernation and arrested death for prolonged periods; un‑ limited transplantation possibilities; and a very wide range of mind‑ modifying techniques, not only drugs but electrical effects, imperceptible odours and the like. If the artificial placenta has not been perfected in phase one, it now will be and naturally produced offspring will be brought to term on it. In addition, we shall see the start of life‑copying. Living organisms will be produced by putting together units of life derived mainly from breaking down living systems; into these organisms a steadily increasing proportion of fully synthesized material will be in‑ corporated. An impact will be made on the problem of prolonging youthful vigour. Hibernation and other storage methods will become practical. The first cloned animals will be produced.

Not till phase three should I expect to see the synthesis of life, control of ageing or a disembodied human brain. Above all, I think that it will take at least this long for genetic engineering to become practical. But all these things should reach fruition, unless war or politics or disaster drasti‑ cally change the present curve of development, within the lifetime of those now young, and a few of those who are not so young.

TABLE OF DEVELOPMENTS

The dates are those of technical achievement, not of general availability, which depends on social and economic considerations.

Phase One: by 1975
> Extensive transplantation of limbs and organs
> Test‑tube fertilization of human eggs
> Implantation of fertilized eggs in womb
> Indefinite storage of eggs and spermatozoa
> Choice of sex of offspring

Extensive power to postpone clinical death
Mind-modifying drugs: regulation of desire
Memory erasure
Imperfect artificial placenta
Artificial viruses

Phase Two: *by 2000*

Extensive mind modification and personality reconstruction
Enhancement of intelligence in men and animals
Memory injection and memory editing
Perfected artificial placenta and true baby-factory
Life-copying: reconstructed organisms
Hibernation and prolonged coma
Prolongation of youthful vigour
First cloned animals
Synthesis of unicellular organisms
Organ regeneration
Man–animal chimeras

Phase Three: *after 2000*

Control of ageing: extension of life span
Synthesis of complex living organisms
Disembodied brains
Brain–computer links
Gene insertion and deletion
Cloned people
Brain–brain links
Man–machine chimeras
Indefinite postponement of death

A recent objective study of current trends arrived at not dissimilar conclusions. Eighty-two experts took part in the study, which was conducted by Olaf Helmer of the Rand Corporation and T. J. Gordon of Douglas Aircraft, who fed the forecasts back to the participants and refined the prediction. These specialists put drugs producing personality changes some sixteen years ahead but, more optimistic than me, expect

THE FUTURE, IF ANY

to see primitive forms of life created in the laboratory by 1989 and the control of hereditary defects by gene engineering by 2000. More cautious than me, they don't expect long-term coma until 2050, nor do they see intelligence being raised by drugs until 2012, with brain–computer links soon after. But, like me, they don't expect extension of life until the same date, when they foresee 50 years being added to the expectancy. They put regeneration of limbs and organs down for 2007. Rather oddly, to my mind, they don't see the breeding of intelligent animals (to replace human labour) until 2050: I should expect this to come earlier than drugs for raising human intelligence, since these drugs will probably be tried out on animals before they are used in man; indeed, this is already occurring.

So it seems certain that many of these advances will occur in the life-time of those now middle-aged and nearly all in the lifetime of those now young. But how far are they in fact problems?

It is rather easy to sensationalize the issues, and some writers have already done so. Thus A. Rosenfeld in *Life* suggests that women may go into a kind of supermarket containing day-old frozen embryos and shop around for the one they want. Presumably there will be a glamorized 4-colour 3-D picture of the adult expected on the pack, as when one buys a package of seeds. For my part, I think this most unlikely. We already have frozen semen, but it is not sold at the dime-stores or do-it-yourself shops. It is obtained only by doctors at their discretion, which they exercise with restraint. Anyone who wants an implanted embryo will no doubt have to take a similar course and persuade her doctor – though, as the process becomes familiar, little persuasion may be called for; it may be more like requesting a smallpox injection. But if any firm were to attempt marketing frozen semen, the state would intervene and a web of legal and conventional codes would be invoked to stop them. The firm's advertisements would be refused, and their other products might be boycotted. No firm of repute would risk tarnishing its image by uncon-sidered, headlong action in such a field.

However, the realities are alarming enough.

More realistically, we might distinguish between those advances which create problems which are probably within the scope of society to handle and those which, like the atom bomb in physics, create problems of a totally new order.

In the first category I would place such matters as specification of the sex of offspring, use of stored eggs and spermatozoa, and even the bringing of babies to term on artificial placentas. It is possible that the power to determine sex might lead to a gross disproportion of the two sexes, but not particularly likely, unless the technique becomes available to coun/ tries, like India and China, where sons are greatly preferred to daughters. Since this would in any case cause a limitation of population, the im/ mediate effects would be desirable rather than otherwise. Professor Leder/ berg has expressed the view that the sex ratio might fluctuate violently, as a result of over/correction of a trend to one extreme, then the other. But with computers, adequate prediction should not prove difficult, and there is no evidence that more than a minority of the population would use such techniques.

Even the bringing of infants to term on artificial placentas does not pose insuperable problems. It is true that there is a real and important task in providing children thus born with the requisite parental love and care. And there is no moral justification for exposing even one child to an inadequate background in this respect. But the requirements are well understood, and the number of cases should be small. Most people will prefer to have children in the normal way, or, if that is not possible, by inovulation.

On the other hand, while discounting some of the wilder bogy/ raising, there are developments which I have described which raise issues far more fundamental than these.

Four strike me as particularly fearsome. First, the development of techniques, probably quite near, for dramatically raising intelligence. Once a few highly intelligent children are born and have reached the age at which they win academic honours and get plum jobs, parents every/ where will begin to scream for the same treatment for their newborn or unborn babies. On grounds of national interest, the state may decide to foster such a trend. Once the level of intelligence rises widely, the educational system will have to be revised. Meanwhile, an élite group will have come into existence. However, perhaps the new race of super/ minds will soon find the answers to the problems created by their own existence.

Secondly, a drastic extension of the life span or even of youthful vigour would cause tremendous social and economic repercussions. Medical services would have to be re/adjusted, retirement practices changed.

Markets would alter. But in addition, the life of the young would suffer a severe impact from the existence of a preponderance of active older people. Already, the rub is felt by couples who do not inherit money from their parents until long after the phase at which it would be most useful. When parents survive to 80, their children may be over 50 before they inherit, and the costs of raising a family have been met. If survival to 150 occurs, with intermediate generations at 120, 90 and 60, most young couples will have not only grandparents, but great-grandparents and great-great-grandparents to visit, look after, and put up with.

The remaining two I will indicate more shortly, since they have already been discussed at length: the prospect of the indefinite postponement of death and the power to modify heredity. Economics cannot cope with the first, nor politics with the second.

Specific consequences

So what? That these changes represent a serious challenge, even a threat, has now been asserted by so many statesmen of science as to amount to a cliché. The matter has been analysed in rather more detail by the late Lord Brain, the eminent English neurologist, in his book *Science and Man*. As he points out, as long ago as 1932 Alfred North Whitehead asserted, 'A muddled state of mind is prevalent. The increased plasticity of the environment for mankind, resulting from the advances in scientific technology, is being construed in terms of habits of thought which find their justification in the theory of a fixed environment.'

'This truth', comments Lord Brain, 'has been overwhelmingly illustrated by the history of the thirty years which have passed since Whitehead wrote these words. The potentialities of science and technology for the benefit of mankind as a whole are almost inconceivably great, but the preparations which we are making for their use and development are pitiably small.'

An outstanding example of our failure to predict and prepare for the consequences of scientific development, he continues, has been population growth. Take, for instance, the demand for physicians. 'It is clear that we shall need many more doctors in thirty years' time. This means more medical schools. It takes a minimum of fifteen years to turn a first-year medical student into a consultant.' It follows that in every westernized country we must start increasing the intake without delay. We are not doing so.

But the prophets who issue these blood-chilling warnings don't give us much to chew on; they remain unhelpfully vague about just how these changes might affect us, and what to do about it.

In this last chapter, then, let me try to spell out in more detail than most prophets care to risk just what I think the consequences of biological innovation might be.

Most authorities have laid stress on the moral implications, but these have a way of solving themselves. It is the moralists rather than morality who stand to suffer most. As Canon Tiberghien has said: 'Moralists may have to pronounce upon these questions, but woe to the world if, when they are consulted, they cannot agree among themselves.' Moral systems firmly based on the golden rule need not be affected, even if they may have to be rephrased, for humanism is rooted in a definition of man which biology has shown to be, to put it mildly, vulnerable. But moral systems which preserve pre-rational tribal taboos, because they are soothing to deeply ingrained unconscious prejudices, and seek to endorse them with divine authority, will simply be overtaken by events, as they have always been in moments of crisis. The institutions which support them will either transform themselves or become obsolete.

The aspect which, in my view, may well prove the most dramatically important is one to which little or no attention has so far been paid: I mean the politico-economic angle.

Before long, I predict, we shall see a tremendous demand developing for the kind of biomedical aids and services which I have described – to say nothing of others still to be devised. A great part of the nation's productive capacity will eventually be devoted to providing prosthetic devices, brain-treatments, transplant operations and so on. It is estimated that in the U.S.A. 1500 transplant operations *a day* may eventually be called for. If society is slow to meet this demand, the response could be violent. People are powerfully motivated where their health and survival and those of their children are concerned.

Some readers may feel that this problem can be left to solve itself; that, as the demand develops, the productive machinery will adapt accordingly. Such complacency, if it exists, is unjustified. The problem is already upon us. The productive machinery is sluggish in adapting. And people are dying in consequence, already.

The case of kidney dialysis deserves most careful attention, not only because it is important in itself, but also because it provides us with an indication of what is to come. It is but the first in a series of such situations. Let us look at the figures. In Great Britain, some 7000 people die of kidney disease each year. Let us exclude all people over 55 and under 16 and assume, conservatively, that only 2000 of these 7000 are suitable for treatment by dialysis, which they would require twice a week. Even if each patient survived only five years, this would build up to some 10,000 patients on dialysis, and average survival might be much longer than this. The first 2000 would cost about £3,500,000 to maintain, and so on for larger numbers, e.g. £17·5 m. for 10,000, a minimum estimate.* The number would be reduced, of course, if some received kidney transplants – but a corresponding increase in special germ-free surgical facilities would be required. To provide surgical facilities capable of handling up to 2000 patients a year would call for an increase in current facilities of many thousands per cent, as well as the training of numerous surgical teams. There is no supply of idle surgeons, anaesthetists and nurses on which to draw for such an expansion. They would have to be recruited and trained *ab initio*, a process requiring many years.

In the case of the U.S.A. it has been estimated that the demand could build up to 20,000 (2000 ideal patients surviving an average of 10 years) or 150,000 (5000 patients a year surviving 30 years) people on dialysis in the U.S.A. On the more conservative figure of 20,000 the cost might be $140 m. a year.

'What is actually happening is that only a minute fraction of the patients with irreversible renal failure get either dialysis or transplantation, on the one hand because of the lack of money and machines, or on the other because no suitable living donor is available and a cadaver kidney cannot be obtained in time. And so they die, often quite young.' These are the words of Professor M. F. A. Woodruff and he adds: 'I am aware of the magnitude of the problem, but I am amazed that so many people appear to be indifferent to this unnecessary loss of life.'

* Nevertheless, Britain used to spend the equivalent of some £50 m. annually on maintaining tubercular patients and still spends £28·5 m. maintaining mentally deficient children, so this is not really out of the question.

This indifference, I believe, arises from ignorance. Many of those affected still fail to realize that their lives, and those of their friends and relatives, could actually be saved. When this realization strikes home, there could be a major public outcry. But all this refers only to the limited field of kidney replacement. When livers, limbs, endocrines and even hearts are added, the load will be beyond anything we can conceive. Society will have to decide whether it wants life and health more than motorways and moon-rockets, and may well prefer the former.

A sign of the times is the appearance in increasing numbers of patient associations – for sufferers from multiple sclerosis, and similar deadly diseases. Such organizations serve a useful purpose in seeing that opportunities for research and treatment are not neglected, and might become politically important, in the kind of way that trade unions have been politically important in the past. In the U.S.A. has been seen an even more interesting trend: the formation of societies for the extension of life, such as the Prolongevity Institute and The Society for Artificial Internal Organs.

Here we see a group of the public pressing for novel biomedical advances, in a manner analogous with the role of the American Rocketry Society and the British Interplanetary Society thirty years ago. Their initiatives led to the National Aeronautics and Space Administration. Will the initiative of these new societies lead to the establishment of a National Biomedical Administration?

Currently, it is often said that we lack a 'mathematics of mercy' by which we can calculate who, of thousands of sufferers, should receive the privilege of being saved by scarce facilities. In Seattle, where kidney dialysis has been pioneered, it has been thought necessary to form a committee of citizens to make these judgments. No doubt this has been motivated, at least in part, by the natural desire of doctors to reduce the terrible and most unfair strain of having to make such decisions single-handed. In Britain, a parallel situation has already arisen in Birmingham, and the Minister of Health has issued guidance on how he thinks these decisions should be handled. As more dialysis machines become available, this situation will be reproduced elsewhere. I find it difficult to believe that it will be accepted calmly by those concerned.

In making such decisions, the natural response is to set up criteria which eliminate as many cases as possible: absence of other disease, younger persons preferred to old, and so on. Such criteria, by making the decision automatic, remove the frightful onus of having to decide on the basis of one's total impression of the human beings concerned. If one knows, for instance, that one candidate is an instigator of racial hatred, while the other has devoted his life to the service of his fellows, it is natural to wish to save the latter rather than the former. Where the difference is less clear-cut the decision is harder.

The fact is, of course, that we do not need a mathematics of mercy – we just need more kidney-dialysis machines.

In the U.S.A. Dr Belding H. Scribner, declaring that it would 'court disaster' not to bring such problems out into the open and face them squarely, devoted his presidential address to the American Society for Artificial Internal Organs to the moral and ethical problems exposed by four years' work with artificial kidneys in Seattle. During this time, he declared, more than 10,000 'ideal candidates' had died for lack of treatment. In the whole U.S.A. there were at that time (1964) between 50 and 100 people on treatment. Patients who can learn to treat themselves will survive, he said; others will die.

And he made the additional point that even for the patient whose disease is too far advanced for a cure, with dialysis he can die with dignity and a minimum of pain. Without dialysis, uraemia leads to a slow, agonizing death – 'one of the most horrible known, sometimes involving many months of intense suffering and great expense'.

Early in 1967 the British Minister of Health, Mr Kenneth Robinson, publicly announced that the British Health Service would provide kidney dialysis equipment as fast as staff to operate it and buildings to house it could be obtained, but that this would be necessarily slow. He revealed that the number of persons currently receiving treatment was 116! He envisaged that a further 60 or so might be treated by new units which were approaching completion.

Fewer than 200 out of a potential demand of at least 2000: this means 1800 people condemned to death in one year, owing to lack of forward planning by the Ministry of Health. (Dr H. de Wardener of Charing Cross Hospital Medical School says the space problem is a red herring.) It is fascinating to me that this appalling announcement was greeted by the House of Commons and the public with the utmost calm. I believe that if in a quarter of a century's time any politician makes a similar confession of ineptitude, he will be howled out of office.

Unless we take action now, this kind of situation could be repeated on many other fronts. Probably the next one will be transplant surgery, and we shall suddenly discover that there are not nearly enough surgeons and sterile wards available to save not only kidney, but heart and lung patients who will die in consequence.

The questions which may have to be raised are: is the political machine adequate and is the economic machine adequate to handle this new kind of situation?

Governments are elected for terms of four or five years, and find it difficult to plan much further ahead. They cannot move far ahead of public opinion, even if they wish, and are influenced by their desire to be returned to power at the next election. Moreover, they are composed of laymen who represent the electorate by their awareness of the current situation, not by their ability to foresee future situations. When they call in expert advice, they constantly reject it, as history repeatedly shows, if it goes against the needs of the moment.

A particularly critical instance of governments' inability to cope with large sociological issues is provided by the population problem. Governments always opt for population increase, since a decline in population creates immediate economic difficulties.

These developments may also profoundly challenge the role of industry. Industry is well adapted to supply relatively portable objects which can be sold at a fixed price. It could therefore manufacture heart and limb prostheses, for instance, very efficiently. It is not adapted to provide medical services, including treatments for improving intelligence or prolonging life and vigour. Though hospitals, in past times, were often started by private or charitable enterprise they have come in the modern world to be accepted as a public responsibility of city or state. But if the future brings biomedical services which are not strictly essential – brain treatments are a good example – will these be provided by state or private enterprise? If biomedicine becomes a major activity, it could make the state a major entrepreneur.

The new biomedicine may lead also to problems on the international as well as the national scale. The first issue is a moral one: is a country justified in providing for itself such super-services as brain-treatment or life-prolongation when, elsewhere, people are dying of malnutrition and the expectation of life is between 20 and 30 years? Even if they feel excused morally, politically this could become a difficult issue.

Moreover, the effect of such developments will inevitably be to increase the gap between developing and developed countries. If the latter raise their levels of intelligence, they will be able so much the more to outstrip the under-developed countries. The leaders of such countries will not be slow to take the point. The demand for the donation of know-how will be intense, and no doubt the leaders themselves will be the very first to submit themselves for intellectual and physical treatment. Late-comers who get even bigger mental and physical boosts from improved techniques will then be well placed to supplant the first-comers, and political success will depend on having the best doctors. Equally, political self-defence will depend on denying one's opponents such jet-assisted take-off. Medicine will be drawn into politics in a manner recalling the Renaissance – a charming prospect.

The instances just cited make the case for forward planning most vividly, since life and death are involved and the number of people concerned is rather large. The belief that the situation will eventually adjust itself is little consolation to those who are dying or to their relatives. The legal and social implications are less obviously dramatic and harder to quantify – a death appears in the national statistics, a lifetime of misery does not – but just as important in their way. The law remains uncertain, as we have seen, on many important points – even the simple question of whether a child born by artificial insemination is legitimate. If it takes the lawyers half a century to modernize the law so it can handle these new situations rationally and unambiguously, many thousands of people will go through unnecessary worry, expense and deprivation. There is absolutely no excuse for a policy of wait-and-see, but that is what is happening. To the best of my knowledge, no government or group of lawyers has taken any initiative to consider this problem, as it affects the private individual – though some steps have been taken towards protecting the medical profession, as we have seen earlier.

Legal issues may become dramatically important when man–animal chimeras are constructed. What will be the legal status of a creature with human chromosomes but animal appearance? And conversely? Human nature being what it is, men will be more horrified at the killing of a

creature which looks like a man but is not, than when the reverse com/
bination is the victim, though reason would suggest the opposite. How
shall we define man? How man/like need one be to qualify for human
benefits, including access to the retirement pension or to union member/
ship? It is not fantasy to say that in our lifetime unions may be faced with
competition from intelligent apes, which may make British coal/miners'
objection to Polish miners, and American racial difficulties, look like
child's play.

These are some of the immediately foreseeable consequences. There are
others more remote and uncertain about which one cannot legislate yet;
it remains to be seen whether, when the time comes, these will be dealt
with any more deftly. One of the more serious of these, I suspect, may be
the creation of élite groups, or haves and have/nots: privilege is always
unpopular, but takes on peculiar importance when applied to life/
prolongation or raising of intelligence. As I suggested in an earlier chap/
ter, it may be only a decade before we have a supernaturally intelligent
élite, with very little ability to find common ground with normal, un/
improved men.

Social cohesion

But in addition to specific effects of this kind, varying with the particular
biological development under consideration, there are others of a more
general nature, no less important because less tangible.

Chief of these is the fact that the outlook as a whole presages an un/
precedented amount of *change* – change in customs and attitudes, change
in capital provision and current expenditure, change in training and job
allocation, change in the tasks and responsibilities of government and
much more. Now there are limits to the amount of change which any
society can absorb in a given time. A high rate of change creates stresses,
even when the change is for the better. Man is a conservative animal, and
the machinery of the law, social customs, technological provision are only
modified slowly. We can see this if we consider, say, motor transport. We
wait until roads are clogged with traffic before we consider building new
ones. Then there is a prolonged period of discussion, funds are gradually
made available, and so on. During all this response/lag, the situation gets
worse. Often the remedy is already obsolete by the time it is applied.

The sluggish nature of social response is derived from the sluggish nature of the individual's response, and his tendency to hope that any problem, if ignored, will go away. In a slightly deeper sense, men never completely unlearn the assumptions and patterns acquired in youth, and progress depends upon their removal by death – a thing which has often been demonstrated in the history of science. It seems likely therefore that the rate at which society can change is keyed in some measure to the average life span. The rising trend of life span is increasing resistance to change, and any major increase would make adaptation far more difficult, perhaps fatally so.

Moreover, change is liable to be frustrating or disturbing in a personal sense. We see this in simple instances such as driving through a section of town we thought we knew and finding new one-way streets or over-passes have been created since we were last there. Man simplifies his life by establishing conventions: we say 'how do you do' because it would be exhausting to devise a new phrase every time. We celebrate weddings or funerals in traditional ways for just the same reason. But when circum-stances change, conventions become obsolete and we have to devise responses on the spur of the moment until new conventions are estab-lished. This can be stressful – as we realize when we find ourselves in a society whose conventions are unfamiliar to us. Biology is about to present us with a vast range of situations for which we have no accepted social responses. (How should one greet a cyborg?)

This is no place for a complete analysis of the consequences of a high rate of change, and I make these points merely to establish the distressing character of rapid social change. One might equally point to the painful economic effects. When a new technology replaces an old one, labour has to be retrained and transferred. But when the car replaced the horse, not every groom converted himself into a mechanic. Unemployment resulted; old skills were wasted; individual human beings felt rejected and un-wanted. To be sure, change cannot be blocked entirely because it will have adverse effects on some. But it is also true that, if change is very rapid, the number of people in society whose lives are impoverished or made painful becomes large. How large a number can we, or should we, tolerate? The wearing nature of industrial society, as we know it today, is largely a result of the high rate of technological innovation. But the social changes generated by biology may impose even greater pressures than do technological changes. Any considerable increase in the change-rate of society might subject the whole structure to severe strain, even bring about collapse.

Finally, while the rate of biological innovation during the next half-century looks like being high, many of the processes thus started will be slow in working themselves out, and the full consequences will not be revealed for several generations. Consequently, society's reaction time will be slow. If a particular hereditary modification proves a mistake, it may take generations to be sure of the fact and several generations more to undo or correct it. The undesirable consequences of prescribing thalidomide to pregnant women became clear within a few years and appropriate steps were taken. Imagine the situation if the problem had not become clear until thalidomide had been used for forty years, and if it had taken forty more to withdraw it again.

We are apt to assume that society exists in its own right: that it will carry on much as before regardless of what we as individuals do. But this is not so. When men live together in groups, they sacrifice certain liberties in exchange for the advantages of mutual aid. The isolated farmer may burn his house down if he wishes. The city dweller is prohibited from doing so, but receives instead the advantages of a fire service. And in general, society functions because people are willing to help it function. A railway can provide padded seating only if people refrain from ruining it, and so on. Of course there are laws which can be enforced against anti-social minorities, when they can be caught. But if the minority becomes too large, it becomes impossible to enforce them effectively. Society is maintained by a constant struggle to control these anti-social elements. When they become too numerous, anarchy results. The socially oriented citizens lose heart and themselves cease to co-operate. If the disorientation continues, the country loses its constructive drive and either disintegrates or is taken over by a more co-ordinated country. This process, so briefly indicated here, we may call *loss of social cohesion*. It has been necessary to outline it, since the problem is scarcely recognized and there is no phrase available to designate it unambiguously.

The kind of massive social disorientation which seems likely to result from the explosion of the biological time-bomb will, I predict, seriously undermine the already somewhat tenuous social cohesion of western countries. Detailed studies of the forces making for cohesion and loss of cohesion are in any case urgently needed, and it is by no means certain that the changes needed to improve cohesion, which may be radical, can be put into effect in time. Some of them at least concern the structure of the family and the attitudes it inculcates in early life: a lag of a generation is thus the minimum before a noticeable change can be effected, and it may well take two generations before the change is well established.

It will be interesting to see whether the dictatorships are able to cope more effectively with such problems. Thus far, they have been notably backward in applying the social sciences. Eventually, the question of whether capitalism or communism survives may depend on their initiative and skill in dealing with these matters.

Coupled with the disorientation of society is a disorientation of personality. In a world in which effort and outcome are not clearly linked – in which the conscientious man is rewarded with injustice and the selfish man gets what he wants – or one where the outcome seems a matter of chance, people lose the incentive to go on trying. Like experimental rats presented with confusing cues, they become neurotic and finally withdraw into a state of tense inactivity. There are already signs of such personal nihilism in society today. It is expressed as cynicism, materialism and a preference for small profits and quick returns. It certainly lies behind the protests and withdrawal from social norms of many of the younger generation – the so-called beatniks, hippies, flower-people and what-have-you. This has been called the Crisis of Consent.

The explosion of the biological time-bomb, unless we take effective steps to channel its energy now, must inevitably foment this nihilism. The new prospects opened up will present people with choices which may prove onerous to take. Responsibility is exhausting.

Today tradition is in bad odour: to describe a practice as traditional immediately suggests that it is obsolete, either an amusing survival or actively harmful. But traditions are devices to simplify decisions. Without them, life becomes impossibly demanding. Our family structure (so different in different cultures) is traditional, and our laws give our traditions force and support. For the new decisions facing people in the post-bomb world, we need new traditions, and a new respect for tradition itself. The deliberate undermining of tradition is one of the forces undermining the cohesion of society.

That these gloomy prognostications are not too unrealistic is suggested by the extraordinary and quite unforeseen consequences which have already attended one biological advance: the synthesis of hallucinogens and brain stimulants. In the thirties, a writer peering into the future might have written of the day, not far off, when one would be able to go to the pharmacist and buy drugs which would stimulate you when tired, calm you when anxious or make you feel good. Indeed, at that time you could actually buy amphetamine sulphate, caffeine and, of course, alcohol for such purposes. What such a writer would not have foreseen would have been that these new drugs would in thirty years have been taken off the open market because a generation had grown up which was quite unable to use them moderately and sensibly.

How has it come about that individuals so devoid of normal good sense as to take sixty times the standard dose of amphetamine at one go have been brought to maturity – if that is the right word?

The instance dramatizes the current failure of our society to instil a social conscience into its members, and gives us a vivid insight into what the future may hold. It seems quite certain that the new powers generated by biology will have to be reserved for a mature and privileged group, to be rationed out only to those who can be relied upon not to misuse them. This is an anti-democratic process, and much to be regretted, but it seems to be the way the world is going.

Some scientists feel that the only sufficiently mature and intelligent group for such a role are the scientists themselves.

The accursed scientist

The day may be approaching when the public turns against science. Currently, the scientist is still the miracle-worker in the white coat, who provides drugs and anaesthetics to relieve our hurts, sources of power and light to ease our labour, and who understands even the secrets of atoms and the stars. But this is a comparatively recent stereotype and behind it lie two others. First, the vague, impractical dreamer who doesn't even know what day it is, so immersed is he in knowledge for its own sake. And then, by extension, the mad engineer, applying his arcane knowledge regardless of the human consequences, causing disasters, manufacturing monsters, prepared even to move the earth from its course or extinguish the sun to test his theories.

To many, the scientist appears as a trouble-maker, poking his nose into things better left obscure, disturbing the established order – at best, a small boy tearing the wings off flies from curiosity, at worst the man whose hallooing sets off the avalanche.

The explosion of the first atom bomb drove a jagged crack through the superman image. From behind the mask of the beneficent father-figure, the mad engineer suddenly looked out, grinning like a maniac.

As the impact of the biological time-bomb begins to be felt, the haunted look of Dr Frankenstein may gradually appear on the faces of the biologists.

At the same time, the very successes of biology create a reputation which becomes steadily harder to maintain. As Professor Rostand has said: 'Yes, of science everything is expected: people believe that, to it, all things are possible. It must make dwarfs grow tall, it must dispense eternal youth, it must supply wit to imbeciles, it must raise the dead.'

The way in which the public looks at science has been gradually changing, however, in a different sense. In the nineteenth century it was seen primarily as a source of material wealth, and this is how it is still seen by many politicians and some of the more old-fashioned, socialistically inclined type of scientist. But it is increasingly appearing as a source of non-material progress. At the same time, it is being increasingly realized that both kinds of science bring problems in their train of a particularly awkward kind, which we are presently ill equipped to solve. The first kind of science has brought pollution of air and water and general damage to the environment. The second has brought the population problem, the arithmetic of mercy problem and others which are as yet barely recognized.

As this process continues, science will begin to be seen in a very dis-enchanted way, as the bringer of gifts which too often end by cancelling their own benefits. The activities of scientists, and their demands for money, will come to be scrutinized much more narrowly than at present, and from a quite different point of view. Instead of asking 'Will this provide us with something we can export, or at least sell?' the question will become 'Will this create for us problems which will nullify any advantage?'

And if really serious adverse conditions develop – there may well arise a solid opposition to science, an anti-scientism the extremer elements in which may demand the prohibition of all scientific activity except under special licence and direct supervision by non-scientific representatives of the state.

The first of the questions which the public is likely to put to the scientists, as the nature of what they are up to becomes clearer, is: why didn't you warn us what was in store?

Various biologists have, in fact, published warnings, though mostly in specialist periodicals, at closed meetings, or in books written at a technical level placing them beyond the comprehension of the ordinary man without a scientific vocabulary. The editor of a widely read general scientific journal said on television recently that he had tried to get scientists to write on these problems, but had been unable to find any who were willing. Some of the warnings sounded in specialist media I have quoted earlier in this book.

Virtually the only warning addressed to the general public in a popularly written book was supplied by Professor Rostand in his *Can Man be Modified?*, originally written in 1956 and available in English from 1959. He was, in fact, far ahead of most other scientists in foreseeing what was coming.

But while a few imaginative scientists have been trying to consider the implications of their work, the great majority never do so, but just carry on from day to day with the problem in hand, recking as little of the wider issues as a bank clerk does of monetary policy.

When pressed to justify himself, in face of the possible misuse of his discovery by society, the scientist generally replies that how knowledge is used is the responsibility of others. Aircraft, he may point out, can be used to drop bombs or to fly sick people to hospital. They are ethically neutral. The way in which they are used is decided by generals and politicians, not by scientists. Knowledge, itself, is always to the good.

This is true, as far as it goes; but it is also true that one does not put matches into the hands of children. Hitherto it has been assumed that the voting citizen and his elected representatives were not children – that is, that they were neither ignorant nor irresponsible. The discovery of nuclear weapons has raised in many minds a genuine doubt whether this is a realistic assumption. This is, socially, a most extraordinary fact, the great significance of which has not been properly appreciated as yet. So profound are the implications that people hesitate to drag them out into the open and face them. It casts in doubt the whole machinery of democracy.

Since, if the state cannot be regarded as responsible, it is difficult to think of any persons or organization that is, one is forced to the conclusion that some knowledge is too dangerous to possess.

It is fashionable to bewail the split between the 'two cultures' and to blame the non-scientist for his ignorance of major scientific principles. But Professor Bentley Glass has cogently argued that the cleavage between the two cultures, at least as far as the academic world is concerned, arises 'not so much because scientists are little interested in the arts, or because humanists are little conversant with the great scientific concepts of the twentieth century, as because the scientist is too blithely confident that more and more scientific knowledge will be good for man irrespective of its applications and too hopefully confident that others can cope with the ethical problems he creates, while the humanist fears the aggrandizement of science in our society and fails to appreciate the nature of the ethical problems that science generates, or perhaps even to recognize their existence.'

While this non-stop sentence (in full, it contains 113 words) is itself indicative of the difficulty scientists have in explaining themselves to the non-specialist, the point is a crucial one, and all the more striking because it is put by a biologist. Biologists, on the whole, prefer to bury their heads in the sand rather than to consider what they should do about the social implications of their own work.

As Dwight Ingle has pointed out, the biologist, and especially the human biologist, is likely to be subject to internal and external pressures, and therefore needs a more independent mind than his colleagues in other disciplines. 'He must be more objective and better able to recognize his primitive emotions and the effect of his childhood indoctrination. He must, in short, be a highly evolved person. Very often he is.' But one must add: and often he is not.

Promethean situation

Man now possesses power which is so extreme as to be, at most, godlike. Prometheus dared to bring down fire from the abode of the gods and give this technique to men, for which he was severely punished. Fire, for all its benefits, was a dangerous acquisition. The myth embodies (as is the function of myths) a lesson: great power constitutes a danger unless used with great wisdom and is therefore reserved to those who know all things and can foresee the consequences of using it. Today mankind is in a Promethean situation. It is precisely because we cannot see, in detail, the consequences of using the new biological powers that they constitute dangers. The fact that they *might* be used for benign purposes or so as to benefit man is not the point, for history shows us that man is far more likely to use power wrongly than rightly.

The fact that some knowledge is potentially dangerous has been recognized by the molecular biologist Professor van R. Potter of Madison, Wisconsin. The only solution to the problem of dangerous knowledge is, in his view, more knowledge. 'From the disorder of unevenly developed branches of knowledge we must achieve some new kind of equilibrium.' And he urges scientists to extend their studies of human adaptability and individuality, and to investigate further the nature of stress and in particular the concept of an optimum degree of stress.

One scientist, it must be conceded, has expressed his doubts even more concretely, but arrives at the contrary conclusion: that there are some things which should not be known.

This is Sir Macfarlane Burnet, the Australian scientist who won the Nobel award in 1960 for his work on tissue transplants. 'It seems almost indecent', says this research scientist, 'to hint that, as far as the advance of medicine is concerned, molecular biology may be an evil thing,' and he concludes: 'It is a hard thing for an experimental scientist to accept, but it is becoming all too evident that there are dangers in knowing what should not be known. But no one has ever heeded the words of a Cassandra.' He argues that work in the field of molecular biology not only ignores possible medical aspects but exposes the world to terrifying dangers. Measles vaccines could be improved, a vaccine could be developed for infectious hepatitis – a major requirement which is still unfulfilled. The practice of culturing viruses and looking for new mutants creates a risk that a dangerous new mutant might escape and set off an epidemic, against which the population of the world would be helpless, since the natural defence systems would be unable to cope with it. 'The human implications of what is going on in this sophisticated universe of tissue-cultured cells, bacteria and viruses which can be grown at the expense of one or other are at best dubious and at worst frankly terrifying.'

The appearance of a serologically unique virus of great virulence 'is a

very serious danger'. If it escaped into circulation without being immediately dealt with the result could be an 'almost unimaginable catastrophe . . . involving all the populous regions of the world'.

Sir Macfarlane Burnet points out that we know very little about why
some viruses or bacteria are so much more lethal than others. The strain
of virus causing myxomatosis in rabbits is 99·7 per cent lethal – perhaps
some newly produced virus affecting humans might be equally potent.
Just as the one virtually wiped out the world's rabbit population, so
the other might all but wipe out the world's human population.

There is also another, subtler danger. As I described in a previous
chapter, viruses can enter cells, carrying with them genetic instructions
which may become incorporated in the genetic material of the host.
These messages are known as episomes. This information may remain in
the cell for several generations in a 'dormant' state, and suddenly –
for reasons which are completely mysterious – may become effective. In
bacteria, such dormant information may kill the host cell when it is thus
switched on, or it may alter it radically.

At present we can only detect that this has happened if the episomal
information kills the cell or makes it malignant.

How can we be sure, Sir Macfarlane Burnet asks, that we are not
introducing episomes into the human genetic material in the course of
molecular biological experiment? He leaves the implications to his pro-
fessional readers to work out, but presumably they include anything from
the sudden appearance of radical alterations in the human genotype –
detectable, it might be, as the appearance of mutant forms, monsters,
defective individuals, a sharp increase in malformations at birth and so
on – to sudden outbursts of cancer or other, perhaps hitherto unknown,
diseases. Just as bacterial cells suddenly dissolve into a pulp because the
viral episome has become active, so perhaps human cells may suddenly
collapse. We might see people age overnight, develop fulminating arthritis,
or disseminated sclerosis. Indeed, some of the disease we see around us
now may spring, for all we know, from such a case.

If there are things which should not be known, should we be prepared
to place some discoveries in the ice box, refusing to make use of them
until we were good and ready? Or should we go even further, and declare
a moratorium on certain branches of research altogether? The possibility
that we might at least pursue the first course has occurred to some scien-

tists. Thus Sir George Pickering, considering the prospect of an indefinite extension of human life, has said: 'I find this a terrifying prospect,
and I am glad I shall be dead and will have ceased to make my own
contributions to this catastrophe before it happens. However, we may
ask ourselves whether it is not time to halt the programme of research and
development which will make such a thing possible. The hint of such
an idea by a man who has spent most of his adult life in research of this
kind savours of intellectual treason. It is inhumane. It is at variance with
the age-old ideas and ideals of the medical profession. Nevertheless, we
should face up to the probable consequences of our ideas and ideals and
be prepared to revise them.'

Another scientist to whom the idea of deliberately refraining from
applying knowledge – in a different field – has occurred is Marshall W.
Nirenberg, the biochemical geneticist at the National Institutes of
Health, whose forecast of 25 years for the realization of genetic surgery
was cited in Chapter 6. Because man will have this knowledge before he
can solve the moral and ethical problems which will be raised, Nirenberg holds that 'When man becomes capable of instructing his own cells,
he must refrain from doing so until he has sufficient wisdom to use this
knowledge for the benefit of mankind. I state this problem well in advance
of the need to solve it,' he says in a letter to *Science*, 'because decisions
concerning the application of this knowledge must ultimately be made by
society, and only an informed society can make such decisions wisely.'

And Rostand has asked: 'Is science reaching a frontier beyond which
its progress might be more harmful than advantageous?' raising the
question of whether a total moratorium on *all* research may not be called
for.

Lord Brain, on the other hand, dismissed this possibility as impracticable, on the grounds that if we cannot foresee the consequences of
scientific discoveries, we cannot foresee the consequences of not making
them either. It follows that man 'certainly has not the capacity to decide
that some particular line of scientific research ought to be abandoned
because of its supposed evil consequences for mankind'. And he adds
that to argue that knowledge can be a bad thing is a waste of time, since
the impulse to know is an inherent part of human nature.

Who, it may be more relevant to ask, is to make the decision, in any
case? Scientists themselves are hardly likely to be unbiased about such a

notion, while commercial concerns doing biological research will be leery of even the ice-box angle. Such decisions will have, naturally, to be taken by governments – but governments feel kindly towards industry and its research efforts, and are unlikely to go very far in this direction. Some powerful and far-sighted body is needed to advise them – a body so prestigious that they will think twice before refusing its advice. With the growth of the social sciences, it is just possible that a strong Social Sciences Council may emerge in some countries, such as the U.S.A., but it is hardly likely to gain sufficient status in time.

Actually, a more powerful argument for the impossibility of such a course is that, while one country might conceivably embark on such a course, world-wide agreement to it would never be obtained. And since without general agreement there would be no point in one country abstaining, they would not do so. It is the fact that there are, or may be, military advantages in biological knowledge which makes it highly unlikely that such research would ever be truly abandoned. At most it might be placed behind barbed wire.

If a moratorium is out of the question, the only alternative is for society to bend every effort towards making an adaptation to the new conditions. How could this be done?

Biological slums

The principal social consequence of the mechanical revolution of the eighteenth century was the crowding of human beings into filthy, disease-ridden slums in the nineteenth – slums which our century spends a great deal of effort in gradually replacing with more civilized conditions. If the biological revolution is allowed to develop unsupervised it will create social conditions causing just as much misery in the twentieth century, which later generations will have to struggle to undo – if there are any later generations, and if they have the needed resources. But, unlike the industrial revolution, the results will not be confined to a few western countries: the whole world will probably become one vast biological slum, no whit less dreadful for being intangible.

One opening step might be the setting up of a research corporation on the lines of the Rand Corporation: we might call it Strand, for Socio-Technological Research and Development. But obviously numerous and varied initiatives are required. Universities should be establishing chairs of social prediction. Philanthropists should be financing research studies. Legal, economic and theological bodies should be organizing conferences to consider the implications.* But before this can occur, considerable propaganda is required to alert people to the problem. As yet, most people don't even know there *is* a biological revolution.

It is time scientists passed from uttering individual warnings couched in general terms to detailed consideration of specific issues. Some begin to realize this. Thus Professor Luria said, at the symposium on the future of medicine referred to below, 'I would not think it premature . . . to establish committees on the genetic direction of human heredity.'

The time is more than ripe, I submit, for such bodies as the National Academy of Sciences in the U.S.A., the Royal Society in Great Britain, and the equivalent bodies in Russia, France and elsewhere, to set up committees to consider how to handle the problem of responsibility in general, and the biological revolution in particular.

A sign of their dawning awareness of this new responsibility is the setting up of committees to consider questions of medical ethics and of experimentation on human beings. In 1966 the AMA held the first National Congress on ethics, after which the US Public Health Service gave a substantial financial grant to the AAAS to investigate the latter problem, following public concern at experiments involving the implantation of cancer cells in hospital patients without their informed consent. The AAAS called in lawyers, sociologists, clinics and doctors to advise. But, as we have seen, the field is enormously wider than mere questions of medical ethics.

In his presidential address to the Royal Society in 1964, Sir Howard Florey raised the issue of the social responsibilities of science in a typically cautious manner. 'Ought we as a society', he said, 'to be considering how science and scientists can contribute to the great problem of bringing the

* In 1963 the CIBA Foundation, set up by a Swiss drug company for the promotion of international co-operation in medical and chemical research, organized a symposium under the title *Man and his Future*. in 1966 the US drug company Merck, Sharp & Dohme organized a symposium under the title *Reflections on the Future of Medicine*. I believe future generations will look back with admiration to these path-breaking initiatives and that the speculations of those taking part will continue to be quoted for a long time.

human population into equilibrium with its surroundings?' and he added: 'I have no doubt myself that we should try to lead scientific advances by positive action.'

Lord Brain has put the matter more forthrightly. 'Our present crises have been produced partly by the activities of scientists. Scientists must therefore seize every opportunity to bring home to those who make the practical decisions about the social organization, the urgency of the problems with which they are faced and their true nature; and, if they can, themselves contribute to their solution.'

And, of course, however well scientists advise political leaders, there is no assurance that their advice will be put into effect. Nevertheless, the advice must be given. For the rest, it is, as H. G. Wells said, a race between education and catastrophe.

Encouragingly enough, there are signs of a change of attitude. In the past few years, in several countries, individuals and groups have formed organizations for studying future trends in a systematic manner, taking both social and technological aspects into consideration. The American Academy of Arts and Sciences, in its journal *Daedalus* (Summer, 1967), published a number of studies of the year 2000 and the first major international meeting devoted to this subject was held in September 1967 under the title *Mankind 2000*. The book you are now reading is itself an indication of this growing awareness that the future cannot just be allowed to happen – but the speculations of individuals will have to give place to comprehensive and systematic studies by teams, using special techniques (such as the Delphi technique developed by the Rand Corporation) to reduce errors and biases and to refine their forecasts.

Conditions of happiness

A primary difficulty in devising plans to meet the problems which biology is conjuring up is constituted by the fact that we have no clear or agreed idea of what kind of world we want. No doubt most people would vote for a social pattern much like the one they know, but devoid of its principal abuses. In the east, this would mean a world of cars and factories and Coca-Cola, without delinquency, ulcers, air pollution or crime. But investigation discloses that the advantages and disadvantages are reciprocally connected. We have air pollution precisely because we have cars and factories to produce goods. We have ulcers because we have a highly competitive productive system which monopolizes the bulk of the time of the bulk of the population. We have delinquency because this kind of footloose society, with its unrestricted communications systems, weakens family control of the young. And so on.

These statements, of course, are mere headlines with which I seek to outline great areas in an attempt to establish a point of view. The actual causes of delinquency, for instance, are complex and it is not my intention to over-simplify them. My point is the large one that all the features of a given society are functionally interconnected, and one cannot change one in isolation from the others.

If, then, we ask ourselves what kind of a society to aim for, on the assumption that we might make a radical change in the pattern, we find ourselves faced with a series of questions to which there are at present no quantitative answers. For example, at what level should we set the density of population so as to avoid either undue isolation or disagreeable over-crowding? In England, with its high population densities, as on the eastern seaboard of the U.S.A. between Boston and Washington, many of the pleasures of life are made difficult or impossible by an absurdly high population density. Yet there are many who are willing to push this process further (cf. Nigel Calder: *The Environment Game*, 1967). Or again, to what extent should we be willing to sacrifice the quality of the environment in order to consume goods? We are busy creating a world in which it is steadily easier to consume goods than to take our pleasure in the form of privacy, a slow pace of work, communion with nature, or doing a job which one enjoys.

Modern industrial methods are making possible a shorter working week, and some authorities have prophesied a working week of twenty hours before the end of the century, with an absolute prohibition on anyone working longer than perhaps thirty hours a week. But why do we have to play it this way? There is no fundamental reason why we should not use this productive margin to redesign the work to make it more interesting. It is quite conceivable that many people would prefer to put in thirty or even forty hours at an interesting task than twenty at a tedious one.

The trouble is, we have simply no method of getting out of the groove. Western society is set up in such a way that increases in productive efficiency automatically show up as more goods; by great efforts over more than half a century we have organized social forces which can cut the supply of goods so as to create more leisure. But to cut it so as to make the job interesting is a trick to perform which no machinery exists.

Then there are more intangible problems, represented by the fact that, in biological matters, we have to plan for several generations ahead. It is not a question of what society *we* want, but what kind of society will our descendants – who by definition will differ greatly from us – want?

Societies consist of people, and it takes a different kind of person to live comfortably in a different kind of society. And vice versa. The hyperactive citizen of today is bored when transferred to a slower-paced society. The slower-paced man is anxious and unhappy when transferred to a hyperactive society. But this does mean that we must consider designing a society which *we* might find uncongenial, if we feel that man might adapt to it, and would be happier for doing so.

The root of our problem, pragmatically, is the absence of any means of measuring satisfaction. And our tendency to assume that an economically calculated 'standard of living' is actually a measure of satisfaction. When we read that the output of manufactured goods reached a new peak, we usually assume this made people happier. But if it was achieved by sacrificing conditions of life which they greatly value, it may have made them, on balance, less happy. And by 'conditions' I do not mean merely extrinsic conditions like privacy in an unpolluted atmosphere, but also intrinsic conditions like the intensified level of anxiety, a frustrated emotional life, or an increase in crime.

Yet, as in the economic instance cited above, we have no machinery, existing or in view, capable of reconstructing our society. If it proves profitable to prolong the lives of the old, for instance, it is all Lombard Street to a china orange that we shall prolong them, regardless of what the change in the age-structure of the population may do to our culture. If it is profitable to make man–animal chimaeras, we shall make them. And if memory-deletion offers some appeal, memories will be deleted. The degree of imagination and effort needed to break out of this situation is probably beyond the imagination and flexibility of man, eastern or western, to achieve.

Current indications are that the world is bent on going to hell in a handcart, and that is probably what it will do.

Professor Arnold Toynbee has described our situation as a failure of our emotional development to keep up with our intellectual development. But this is to misrepresent the problem. For there is no sense in which emotion can be expected to accumulate as knowledge does, nor are there emotional techniques which can be handed on ready-made to the following generation. It is more to the point to say that sociological knowledge has not kept up with knowledge in the physical sciences, for there is at least some reason to believe that, with a profounder under-standing of the relationship between culture and personality, one might shift the system in the direction of co-operativeness and social conscience and away from selfishness and aggression. Human societies display a rather wide range between these extremes.

But while primitive societies, which have not learned to challenge their own traditions, may live peaceably and agreeably, it is far from certain that societies with universal means of travel and intensive education can do so. Modern life, as we understand it, may mean an inevitable increase in the proportion of desocialized individuals. But no one can quarrel with the proposition that we urgently need to find out whether this is so, and to learn how to hold disruption to a minimum.

The basic answers lie for all to read in the works of wise men. Man is the measure; knowledge, without the corrective of charity, hath some nature of venom or malignity. It is the know-how for putting these principles into effect which is lacking.

Index

147; work with hormones, 144–5;
decompression, 145–6; distrust of,
155–6; social problems, 207
international relations, 213–14
irideremia, breeding out of, 42
Italy, law on transplantation, 72

Jackson, H., 49–50
Jacob, Stanley W., 104–5
Jacobovits, Immanuel, 116
Jacobson, Allan, work on learning, 137
Jehovah's Witnesses, 74
Joubert, Pierre, oldest man known, 96

Keele, C. A., on pain-relieving drugs,
150
Kelley, W. D., 64
Keynes, Richard, 42
kidney dialysis, 210, 211–12
kidney transplantation, first successful,
56–8; risks of delay, 66; risk for
donor, 73; see also *transplantation
surgery*
Kline, Nathan, on tranquillizers, 128–
129
Knipling, Edward E., 17
Kopac, M. J., and microsurgery, 197
Koprowski, Hilary, 111
Kramer, M., 41
Krech, David, and environmental factor in intelligence, 146–7

Landau, Lev, arrested death of, 113
Lapchinsky, Anastasy G., work on limb
grafting, 63
law, and social behaviour, 132–3; on
new developments, uncertainty of,
214; on artificial insemination, 51–
52; on transplantation surgery,
70–5; on sterilization, 72; on

chimeras, 214–15; see also *illegiti-
macy, social problems*
Lederberg, Joshua, on dangers of biological research, 10; on cloning, 23;
on genetic engineering, 172–3, 177–
178; on balance of sexes, 207
Leeuwenhoek, Anthony van, 43
Lehmann, Heinz, on mood control, 131
Lehr, Herndon B., work on skin
storage, 68
libido, regulation by drugs, 45
lie detector, basis of, 153–4
life, nature of, 189, 200–1; DNA replication in, 191; origin of, 186–92,
196–201; steps in creation, dis-
tinguished, 197; criteria of, 188;
sanctity of, 42, 43
life span, in different species, 96; and
hibernation, 109; extended, patterns
of, 110; social problems of, 123,
207–8; and adaptation to change,
216; see also *ageing*
Lillehei, R. C., 64
Loeb, Jacques, 30
Long, Crawford W., 148
LSD-25, see *hallucinogens*
Luria, Salvador, on genetic surgery, 10,
177, 183, 227
lysosomes, role in cell death, 97

McCay, C. M., 98, 99, 110
McConnell, James V., 135–6
machines, intelligent, attitudes to, 88–9
McKay, Donald, 111, 156–7
'*man-amplifier*', 82–3
Mark, Vernon, 148
marriage, separated from sexuality, 45;
see also *family*
'*mathematics of mercy*', 211
Medawar, Sir Peter, 7, 59–60, 61